Communicati(

& Language

Activities

Running Groups for School-Aged Children

Communication & Language Activities

Running Groups for School-Aged Children

Hackney Speech & Language Therapy Service
Edited by Sarah Nash

HINTON HOUSE Classroom Resources

HINTON HOUSE

First published by

Hinton House Publishers Ltd,

Newman House, 4 High Street, Buckingham, MK18 1NT, UK

T +44 (0)1280 822557   F +44 (0)560 313 5274
E info@hintonpublishers.co.uk

www.hintonpublishers.co.uk

© Hackney Speech & Language Therapy Service for Children, 2013

First published 2013
Reprinted 2014 (twice), 2015

The right of Hackney Speech & Language Therapy Service for Children to be identified
as the author of this work has been asserted by them in accordance with the Copyright,
Designs and Patents Act 1988.

British Library Cataloguing in Publication Data

A CIP catalogue record for this book is available from the British Library.

ISBN 978 1 906531 52 2

Printed in the United Kingdom by Hobbs the Printers Ltd

This book is dedicated to the hundreds of teaching and learning support assistants who have been running language groups tirelessly in Hackney over the past decade. With your assistance we have made, and will continue to make, a difference to the communication skills of children and young people in East London.

Contents

Part Two: Resources

Acknowledgements

This book is the result of teamwork over many years. The idea for the resource was developed by Katy Ahern and Katharine Dent, speech and language therapists, in 1999. It has been added to, tweaked, changed and overhauled many times in order to provide staff in schools with as many ideas as possible to deliver communication and language groups. Many speech and language therapists and specialist teachers who work in Hackney have participated in its development, adding ideas from their experience with children, or from their creative minds.

It is difficult to know the source of many of these games and activities. We recognise that many of them will be familiar to people working with children and so may not be our original ideas. This resource is designed to pull together the many and varied activities that speech and language therapists and other professionals use with children regularly.

I would like to extend particular thanks to Stephen Parsons, who contributed many of the new ideas for this book, and who has encouraged me for a long time to have it published.

Sarah Nash, Editor
Speech and Language Therapist
Children's Integrated Speech & Language Therapy Service for Hackney and the City
www.gethackneytalking.org.uk

Introduction

Good communication is a fundamental life skill for learning and social interaction. Small groups have been shown to be an effective way to support and develop children's communication skills. Research has shown that children with speech, language and communication needs (SLCN) benefit from language intervention that involves their peers.[1]

This resource is designed to support anyone who works with children to independently plan and deliver a communication group. A communication group is a regular, protected, friendly and fun environment where children can learn and explore language and build their confidence in communicating. It provides an opportunity for children to develop and practise important foundation skills for language and learning, such as listening and turn-taking. Communication groups are also a useful and effective way for children with communication and learning difficulties to develop specific language skills.

All children can benefit from attending a communication group, but children who have communication difficulties will especially gain from them. Communication groups can be used with children who have a range of needs, including language delays, language disorders, learning difficulties, autistic spectrum disorders, speech production difficulties and neurological disorders such as cerebral palsy. Groups can be planned and adapted for children who are non-verbal or who use Alternative and Augmentative Communication (AAC), such as signing or voice output communication aids (VOCAs).

Small communication groups work well in schools and can be delivered by almost anyone, from teachers, teaching assistants and special needs coordinators to learning mentors and speech and language therapists. Some of the activities in this resource can also be adapted for use in the classroom with a whole class of children. Communication groups can also be run in after-school clubs.

Communication groups can be run outside the school environment too. Parents may like to use these activities in the home to develop their children's language and interaction skills. They could be even be used at parties, or in community group settings such as Scouts or Brownies.

---

1 Law, J., Garrett, Z., & Nye, C., 2004, 'Speech and language therapy interventions for children with primary speech and language delay or disorder', *Cochrane Collaboration Database of Systematic Reviews* 2009 (4), CD004110.

Getting started

Choosing group members

All children can benefit from a communication group, but it is important to think about who the group is for. Choosing target children who need to develop specific language skills will enable a clearly focused group to be planned and delivered. Other children who are peers from the school class or year group can then be included around the target child. Groups work best with a maximum of about six children.

Try to consider the personalities of the children and ensure that you have a good mix. Children who are shy can benefit from the safe environment of a group, which may encourage them to interact more with their peers. Those who are new to learning English, or who are bilingual, may benefit from the communication group as an opportunity to learn and practise their new language skills and to experience positive social interaction.

Communication groups are a great space for children who have attention and listening difficulties to develop the foundation skills for learning, such as looking and sitting appropriately, but you may also find it can be useful to include some children who are good role models for these skills too.

Finding a space

A quiet space that is free from distractions will help a communication group to run smoothly. However, finding a space like this can be a challenge in a busy school environment! Using the same area each time will allow children to become familiar with the expectations for the session.

For younger children of around three to five years old, sitting on the floor in a circle will work best; it is important that there are not too many objects or distracting materials nearby. Older children will be able to sit on chairs around a small table, which is more appropriate to the expectations of the classroom environment. However, some activities in this resource involve moving around the room, so finding a space that has capacity for this would be useful.

Planning for length and frequency

Communication groups for children in the early years (i.e., under-fives) should ideally run for around twenty minutes. Some children may not be able to listen and attend for this length of time initially, but should be able to build up to it over time. Older children of primary school age should be able to take part in a group lasting for about thirty to forty minutes.

If possible, groups should be run at least once or twice per week, but if they can be held more frequently it would be beneficial. However, more important than the frequency of the group is the carry-over of the skills learned to environments outside the group. See the section below, 'Carry-over to other environments', for ways to do this.

It is also important to agree and plan extra time for the group leader to get ready before the group begins, and to allow some time to reflect and evaluate the session afterwards: ten minutes is suggested as a minimum.

Planning the session

Communication groups work well when a structure is followed for each session. A suggested format is outlined below.

Hello and warm-up game	Start with a warm-up game, which is a fun way to encourage the children to interact with each other.
Group rules and visual timetable	Introduce or recap the group rules and set expectations for the session. Talk through the visual timetable to show children what is coming up.
Target activity(ies)	Include any number of target activities linked to the areas of language and communication that the children need to develop. For longer groups more activities may be included, or activities can run for longer.
Cooling-off game and rewards	Finishing with another rewarding game will help the group to end positively.
Goodbye	Close the session, encouraging group members to say goodbye to each other.

Following this familiar structure for each session will allow children to anticipate what might happen next and to feel secure.

The structure of the session should also be shared with children visually. The use of a visual timetable is recommended, so that the children can see what is coming next (see 'Template for Visual Timetable' in the Resources section, p. 203). A visual timetable can use symbols, pictures or just written words for those who can read. It is also a helpful prompt for the group leader to get ready for the next activity. Once each activity has been completed it should be removed from the visual timetable. The members of the group could physically remove a symbol or simply cross the words or pictures off the list.

Example of a visual timetable

Written version	Symbol version
1. Throw the Beanbag	
2. Who is Wearing the Hat?	
3. Big Box	
4. Barrier Game	
5. Fishing for Pictures	
6. Goodbye	

Group rules

It is useful to establish group rules to encourage active listening and good behaviour. These rules can form the basis of positive feedback to the children, as well as being behaviour management prompts. Suggested basic rules are:

❖ Good looking
❖ Good listening
❖ Good sitting
❖ Wait for your turn

These rules are represented visually on cards in the Resources section of this book (see Resources, Group Rules Cards, p. 198).

Group rules help children to understand the behaviours you expect from them. Different rules may be introduced if a child is having a specific difficulty. Try to ensure that rules are phrased positively: for example, 'Keep your hands on your lap', rather than negatively, as in 'Don't touch other children'.

Specific communication targets

The main target activities in a communication group should be chosen to link to a particular skill that the children need to develop. The 'Indicators of difficulty' page in each section of this resource can help to identify which areas of communication to focus on in the group. Information about a child's specific needs could also be gathered from a speech and language therapist or teacher.

Short-term targets should be set for the children for the period that the group runs. Each section in this book has a list of targets that reflect a development of skills within that particular area of communication. Each activity also has a clearly described aim. Activities for each group session should be chosen by selecting those which have aims linked to the child's short-term communication targets. Targets should be set so that they are sufficiently challenging. The group sessions will enable children to practise and build up to the target.

Three to four targets should be selected, linking to the children's areas of need. Having a mixture of targets from different language and communication areas can provide variety, but groups can also be designed to develop just one aspect of communication (e.g., vocabulary).

It is suggested that the same targets are set for around six sessions, and that different activities to practise each skill are planned for. It is fine to repeat the same activities in order to develop a skill, but also important to recognise when children have achieved their targets and it is time to move on.

Keeping a record of each child's progress towards their short-term communication targets after each session will enable the group leader to know when a child has achieved their target. Spending five to ten minutes afterwards to complete a record sheet will allow time to reflect on whether the children could achieve the aims of the activities, and also to make plans for the next session.

A template for a group record sheet is provided in the Resources section along with an example of a completed record sheet (see Communication Group Record Sheet, p. 199 and Sample Group Record Sheet, p. 200). This can be photocopied and the chosen targets should be filled in before starting a group.

Developing Good Communication in Groups

When running a communication group with children it is important to facilitate their communication to help them develop new skills. Below are some top tips for ways to support good communication in groups, as well as ways to make the groups run smoothly.

❖ Gain eye contact and ensure children are listening to you by saying their name before you give an instruction.

❖ Break down verbal instructions into small steps. Children with language difficulties often cannot remember or process more than one piece of information at a time. It is especially important to remember this when explaining how to do each activity.

❖ Use visual clues whenever possible to assist the children in understanding and recalling information. These may be pictures, real objects, photographs or symbols. This is particularly important because a child's memory and sequencing skills may well be impaired.

❖ Use gesture or signing together with speech. Natural gestures like pointing or holding a hand up to mean 'stop' will support the children's understanding of what you mean when you say these words. Using signs such as those from the Makaton language programme can provide a familiar clue to the meaning of the words you say.

❖ Check that the children have understood your question/instruction by asking them to repeat what they have to do. Give them a way to show you when they have not understood (e.g., by putting their hand up). Think about why they might have failed to understand, for example:

  ❖ the sentence was too long;

  ❖ the sentence contained vocabulary that they did not know;

  ❖ the words used have more than one meaning (e.g., 'male' vs. 'mail'); or

  ❖ the sentence structure and order of words was confusing (e.g., 'Before you change places can I ask you to remove the last picture from the visual timetable?').

❖ Be repetitive in your teaching of new concepts/vocabulary. Use different games to teach the same vocabulary and say the words many times – children need to hear a word frequently before it is embedded in their vocabulary.

Page 1 of 2

Developing Good Communication in Groups

❖ Encourage children to expand on what they say, using more detailed and complex language.
For example:

   ❖ Child: 'I went to the shops.'
   ❖ Adult: 'Aha, you went to the shops with …?'

❖ Encourage good turn-taking in the group when talking and playing games. Use the Group Rules to prompt children to do this.

❖ Encourage self-help skills. Make it an expectation that when the children have not understood something they need to ask, 'What did you say?', or 'I don't understand.' This will support children to independently get help, and can be much more useful than 'Huh?', or no response at all.

❖ Prepare and refer to a visual timetable to let the children know what games will be played before the group begins. Showing them the order of the games played helps them to know what to expect. It is useful to use visual symbols or even just written words for children who can read. Look at the timetable together at the beginning of the group and talk about what you are going to do. Tick off, cross out, or remove the symbol from the timetable after each activity is finished.

❖ In order for children to change something that they have difficulty with, they need to know what they are doing right. Using specific praise will help the child to repeat the desired behaviour, for example, 'I really noticed you doing good listening then.'

❖ It is fine to give correction when children have not given the targeted response to an activity. Children need to know when they have not done what you were expecting, so that they can learn and change. Always phrase correction in a positive way and praise efforts for trying or contributing, for example, 'Good try. Have another think.'

❖ When correcting a child's response, you can help and guide them towards the target answer. Ways of doing this include: offering a choice of words (e.g., 'Is it an elephant or a giraffe?'); giving the beginning of the word (e.g., 'It's an el…'); or supplying a description (e.g., 'It's very big, grey and has a long trunk').

Page 2 of 2

Handout 2
Carry-Over to the Classroom & Home

Communication groups are a great way for children to develop specific language and interaction skills. However, it is important that children with communication difficulties learn to generalise their new skills and carry them over to different environments. Below are some suggestions for ways to build on and extend communication group work to the classroom and home environments.

❖ Ensure that the children's class teacher is aware of the specific communication targets that you are working towards. This will allow them to create opportunities to reinforce those particular skills in classroom activities. For example, if you are working on the understanding of 'who' and 'where' questions in the group, the class teacher could make sure they ask the children these specific questions when discussing a story the whole class has just read.

❖ It is essential that the new vocabulary you are targeting in the group can be transferred to other environments. This will help the children to use their new words for a meaningful purpose outside the group. For example, if you are targeting vocabulary about trees and plants in the group, as well as learning about plants in science, share the words that the children have been working on with the class teacher and support staff. Send vocabulary lists home to parents so they are aware of which words to practise and reinforce at home during homework or when the words come up in other contexts, such as in the park or at the shops.

❖ Inform children of their specific communication targets or, better still, involve them in setting targets for themselves. Targets from communication groups should be included on a child's individual education plan so that their teacher and family are aware of these and can focus on them throughout the day.

❖ During group sessions regularly discuss situations in which particular new skills would be applied in the classroom or other environments. For example, if doing an activity on giving instructions, discuss occasions during the week when they might give instructions to other children or adults, such as when getting their little sister to change the channel on TV, or when describing how to do a science experiment to another child in the class.

Page 1 of 2

Handout 2

Carry-Over to the Classroom & Home

❖ Some group activities are easily transferrable to the whole class environment. Train the teacher in how to lead the game and include the whole class in playing it. Communication group games can work well in structured carpet time or circle time sessions, but also when there are five minutes to spare at the end of a lesson or on a rainy day.

❖ Use the active listening group rules in the classroom as expectations for all children (see Resources, Group Rules Cards, p. 198). Symbol cards can be enlarged and displayed on classroom walls, and children could earn rewards points in the classroom when they are seen to be following these rules.

Page 2 of 2

Handout 2

Dealing with Difficulties in Groups

Seating

❖ Children who have difficulties with sitting still tend to rock on chairs, especially if the chairs are not the right size for the child. Ensure that the children are sitting on chairs that are not too big or small. Avoid those with wheels!

❖ To prompt children to sit properly, show them the 'good sitting' card (Resources, Group Rules Card, p. 198) or introduce a specific phrase or gesture that they understand; for example, raise four fingers and say 'Four on the floor' (which means 'Put four chair legs on the floor').

❖ The seating of the group may need to be mixed so a child is not sitting by another who provokes them. Be aware that children seem to really dislike being deliberately moved; instead, start the group with a game that involves moving places. Play this game until the children are appropriately separated.

❖ Include activities that get children to move around in groups, so that those who have lots of energy can use some of it up. Games that involve changing places are also a good way to incorporate movement. A two-minute stretch break can work well in the middle of a group session.

Structure

❖ Children who have behavioural difficulties find a predictable routine useful, as this helps them to know what is expected of them. Ensuring that the beginning and end of a group session are clearly defined will help children to know what to expect, and can reduce disruptive behaviours. Use specific activities such as a hello song, a favourite game and a calming activity at the end to add structure and routine to your sessions.

❖ Use a visual timetable. This shows visually what is happening and what is coming up next, so that children know what to expect.

❖ Children who have difficulties maintaining attention or who have behavioural problems may not be able to cope with a full language group. Start by running very short groups (e.g., ten minutes) and then build up to more activities if they are managing to participate.

❖ When children become bored, challenging behaviour can start. Ensure that you have a fast-paced turnaround of activities to keep children interested and involved.

❖ Most games and activities involve going around the group so that every child has a turn. Keeping to this predictable order helps children to understand turn-taking and encourages them to wait and not call out.

❖ Introducing choice helps children to feel valued in that they have something to contribute. It also helps children who have difficulties following adult direction to feel as if they are somewhat in control. Examples of choice include: allowing the children to choose their own picture card; choosing the order of activities; or choosing a game for the next session.

Praise and rewards

❖ Some children make it obvious when they are doing the right thing; other children are quieter and may be less noticeable when they are doing what you expect. When giving praise be fair, and ensure that all children have opportunities to receive praise from you.

❖ Children who show difficult behaviour also need to experience praise, so look out for opportunities to 'catch them' doing something well.

❖ Rewards should be earned and linked to specific behaviours such as adhering to the group rules. Make prudent use of stickers or rewards at the end of groups, rather than giving out stickers at each session just for showing up. Link rewards to specific positive behaviours. Using a phrase such as 'You're getting a sticker today because [give the reason]', will help the children to see the link between their behaviour and the reward.

❖ Build in a specific reward system for children who particularly need more motivation. For example, use a star chart or a tally of points that leads to a reward at the end of the block of group sessions. There is an example of this in the Resources section, called the 'I am working for …' Chart, p. 205.

❖ Some children have significant behavioural difficulties and often miss out on opportunities to develop their language and social interaction skills because their behaviour excludes them. A communication group is an ideal place for them to develop these skills. However, sometimes you may need to tolerate some oppositional behaviour in order for that child to receive this important group experience.

❖ Use gestures to acknowledge when someone is not following a group rule, rather than constantly repeating the rule. For example, a hand held up to indicate that a child needs to wait their turn provides them with a quick visual cue that they need to wait; this also allows the group discussion to continue without interruption.

Useful Resources for Running Communication Groups

❖ Symbol software programme to create your own visual timetables and picture resources. Many of the games in this resource can be made using symbol programmes in which you type in a word and a pictorial version of that word appears. You could also try using image searches on the internet.

❖ Noun cards, grouped according to categories

❖ Action pictures (verb cards)

❖ Sequencing pictures

❖ Emotion cards

❖ Social situation pictures

❖ Rhyming words picture cards

❖ Listening game CDs, with matching picture cards

❖ Stereo or other music player

❖ Soft opaque bag

❖ 'Posting' box made out of a shoebox

❖ Puppets

❖ Masks

❖ Soft animal toys, such as teddies

❖ Dolls or small human figurines

❖ A 'fishing rod' made of a stick with string and a magnet attached

❖ A collection of common objects such as a cup, pencil, hat, glasses, key, spoon, cloth

❖ Toy furniture

❖ Toy food

❖ Coloured counters

❖ Dice

❖ Game boards

❖ Dressing up clothes, including accessories such as glasses, gloves and hat

❖ Bubbles

❖ Stickers

❖ Colouring pencils, crayons or pens

❖ Musical instruments, such as shakers, bells or drums

❖ Balls

❖ Small beanbags

❖ Wooden or Unifix® bricks

❖ Small boxes or plastic containers

❖ A cloth or a large scarf

❖ Pictures books with interesting busy scenes

❖ Spare paper

❖ Ring binders

❖ Egg timer

❖ String and pegs

Part One
Communication & Language Activities

The Activities

The communication and language activities in this book are divided into sections that emphasise different communication skills. Each section begins with a brief description of the skills, followed by some indicators of difficulty, so that you can recognise when a child needs help in this area.

Each section (apart from Warm-Up Games) also has a list of targets that reflect a development of skills within that particular area of communication. These can be used as short-term targets for the children to achieve by the end of the period that the group runs. Each activity also has a specific aim describing the purpose of the activity, as well as the target communication skill the game is developing within that session. Ensure that you choose activities with aims that link to your short-term targets.

The activities are ordered according to level of difficulty, with the easiest ones first and the harder ones at the end. The equipment you need to run each activity is also listed. If no equipment is listed this means it is an activity that does not require resources. Some of the resources for the activities can be found in the Resources section of this book, others will be items commonly found in the school or classroom environment.

There are also some suggestions on how to adapt the activities to make them easier or harder and some activities include helpful hints to make the games run smoothly.

At the end of each section are some top tips for how to develop and support children in that area of communication in the classroom.

Enjoy the group!

Warm-Up Games

Playing a warm-up game at the beginning of each group session gives children an opportunity to become familiar with each other and to begin taking turns before the learning activities begin. The warm-ups are designed to be simple and enjoyable. They can also be played as rewarding games to finish on, if the children particularly enjoy them.

Hello Song

Expected Time
Quick

Resources needed
None

Challenge level
Beginner

Aim	For children to join in and learn each other's names
Method	Start with a particular child. Encourage all the other children to look at the child who is the focus and to join in singing these words to that child:

'Hello Katy [say the name of the child who is being sung to], how are you?', or 'Hello Katy, hello Katy, hello Katy, it's nice to see you here.'

Move around the group in a clockwise direction until all group members have been sung to. Reinforce the good listening rules by commenting on children who are listening, taking turns, looking or sitting well.

Clap Your Name

Expected Time
Quick

Resources needed
Drum (optional)

Challenge level
Beginner

Aim	For children to recognise and clap or beat the syllables in their name
Method	Pass a drum around the group in a clockwise direction. Greet each child in turn, and then encourage them to beat out the syllables in their name. For example: 'Hen-ry' = 2 beats. 'Mo-ham-med' = 3 beats. If not using a drum, the children simply clap out their name.
Making it harder	The whole group joins in and claps each others' names.

Roll the Ball/Throw the Beanbag

<table>
<tr><td>

Expected Time
Quick

</td><td>

Resources needed
Ball or beanbag

</td></tr>
</table>

Challenge level
Beginner

Aim	For children to take turns, say names, and look at other group members
Method	The children roll a ball or throw a beanbag to each other and, as they do, they say the name of the person they are rolling or throwing it to. For example, 'I am rolling the ball to Sarah.'
	Encourage all children to look at the person they are rolling the ball or passing the beanbag to.
Helpful hint	Remind the children that the ball is to be rolled and the bean bag is thrown gently. Only the child whose name is used can receive the ball or beanbag.
Making it easier	Roll the ball or pass the beanbag without saying names.

'I Like ...'

Expected Time	Resources needed
Quick	None

Challenge level
Beginner

Aim	For each child to join in the group and share something about themselves
Method	Choose a topic in which children can say what they like, such as 'doing', 'eating', or 'watching'. Go around the group in a clockwise direction and encourage each child to say their name and something that they like. For example, 'My name is Ashraf and I like doing drawings'; or 'My name is Mehmet and I like watching Power Rangers'; or 'My name is Jordan and I like eating Monster Munch.'
Making it harder	Ask the children to recall others' names and what they said. This can also be played as a harder memory game by asking the children to say what the others before them said, then adding their own name to the list. For example, 'That is Shona and she likes watching football, that is Kulvinder and he likes watching wrestling, and my name is John and I like watching "The Simpsons".'

Warm-Up Games

Bubbles

Expected Time
Mid-length

Resources needed
Container of bubbles

Challenge level
Beginner

Aim	For children to wait and take turns
Method	Move in a clockwise direction around the group with each child taking a turn at blowing the bubbles. The other children can pop them.
Helpful hint	Children naturally want to get out of their chairs to blow and pop the bubbles. Allow them to do this, but encourage them to all sit down again and wait for the next person's turn.

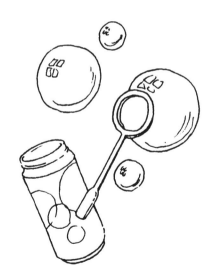

Space on My Right

Expected Time Mid-length	**Resources needed** ❖ A chair for each person ❖ One extra chair
Challenge level Beginner	

Aim	For children to wait and take turns
Method	Start with an empty chair on your right and invite a member of the group to come and sit in the empty chair. Use a consistent sentence to invite them: for example, 'There is a space on my right, and I ask Roshan [name of the chosen child] to sit here.' This then creates an empty chair somewhere else in the group. The person with the empty chair to their right then has a turn. Encourage children to use the whole sentence: 'There is a space on my right, and I ask [say name of the chosen child] to sit here.'
Making it easier	Participants use a simpler sentence, such as, 'Roshan, come and sit here.'

Warm-Up Games

My News

<table>
<tr><td>Expected Time
Mid-length</td><td>Resources needed
Questions Prompts, p. 214</td></tr>
</table>

Challenge level
Intermediate

Aim	For children to report an event
Method	Go around the group and take turns to share news about what everyone has done since the last group session. Start by giving the children an example.
Making it easier	Provide a sentence starter, such as 'At the weekend …', or 'On the school trip …' Write this starter sentence down so you can prompt the children further.
Making it harder	Make this interactive by encouraging the other children to ask questions about what they have heard. Symbol prompts with question words such as 'Who', 'Where', 'When', and 'What happened?' may be useful when doing this.

Count to Ten Together

Expected Time	Resources needed
Quick	None

Challenge level
Advanced

Aim	For children to be able to use eye contact, take turns, and cooperate to complete a task
Method	The aim of this activity is for the group to count to ten. This is not as easy as it sounds! Start counting by calling out 'one'. Then anyone can join in, calling out the next number. The catch is that only one person can talk at a time. If two people say a number at the same time, the group needs to go back and start counting from one again.
Helpful hint	Encourage children to look at each other to judge who is about to say a number.
Making it easier	To make this easier, try counting to five.

$$1 \; 2 \; 3 \; 4 \; 5$$

$$6 \; 7 \; 8 \; 9 \; 10$$

Something Good

Expected Time	Resources needed
Quick	None

Challenge level
Advanced

Aim	For children to engage in conversation with a peer
Method	Ask the children to get into pairs. They then have to talk to their partner and find out one good thing that has happened to their partner during the week. It could also be something good that they have done. Once everyone has had a turn at saying something good, the pairs report back to the group. Each person should describe their partner's good thing.

Make a Connection

<table>
<tr><td>Expected Time
Mid-length</td><td>Resources needed
None</td></tr>
</table>

<table>
<tr><td>Challenge level
Advanced</td></tr>
</table>

Aim	For children to get to know each other and engage in conversation with a peer
Method	Ask the children to get into pairs. The children then need to talk to their partner and share some information about themselves. The aim is to try to find out something that they have in common. Once they have made a connection, the pairs report back to the group. For example: 'We both have a sister', or 'We both think tomatoes are disgusting!'
Helpful hint	This game works best at the start of a new group, when the children do not know each other very well. Try to get children who already know each other to pair up with different people.
Making it easier	Give children some prompts for the sorts of things to say about themselves. For example: 'My family'; 'Where I am from'; 'Things I like doing after school'; and 'What I want to be when I am older'. These could be written on a whiteboard as a visual reminder.

Warm-Up Games

Attention & Listening

Attention and listening skills are extremely important, because they form the foundation of language and learning. This section provides activities that give children the opportunity to practise attention and listening in small groups. It is particularly important to reinforce the group rules of 'good listening', 'good looking', 'good sitting', and 'wait for your turn' (see Resources, Group Rules Card, p. 198). By repeating the rules and reinforcing them through the practical and fun activities, children will have a chance to develop greater control over their impulsivity and be able to extend their ability to listen.

Indicators of Difficulty with Attention & Listening

Children with attention and listening difficulties may display some of the following features:

❖ fleeting attention;

❖ needing support to focus on tasks;

❖ difficulty concentrating on more than one thing at a time (e.g., struggling to listen to instructions whilst colouring in);

❖ difficulty following simple instructions;

❖ difficulty taking turns;

❖ inconsistent response when name is called;

❖ not seeing tasks through to completion;

❖ following own agenda and not responding to verbal demands from others; and

❖ high distractibility; reacting to noises and movement around them

Attention & Listening Targets

1 To look and copy actions

2 To wait and respond to a visual cue

3 To listen and respond to own name

4 To take turns in a non-verbal activity

5 To listen and respond to a word or simple question

6 To follow a command from a sound cue

7 To listen and link sounds to objects

8 To repeat a sentence

9 To use visual memory to identify objects

Do What I Do

Expected Time
Quick

Resources needed
None

Challenge level
Beginner

Aim	For children to look and copy an action
Method	Tell the group to look carefully and do what you do. Silently start making an action and repeat it over and over: for example, a handclap, a finger click, or tapping your shoulders. The children need to look at the actions and copy them. Change from one action to the next without giving warning. If there are children who are not looking they will miss the change in action.
Making it easier	Prompt children to look carefully just before the action is changed.

Attention & Listening

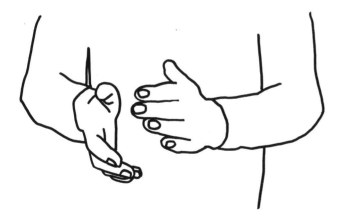

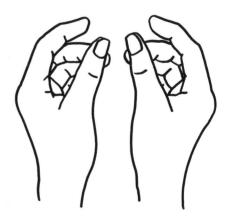

Tower Game

Expected Time
Quick

Resources needed
Stacking blocks

Challenge level
Beginner

Aim	For children to listen and respond to their name in turns
Method	Start building a tower with a few bricks and call out each child's name, in any order. When the child responds to their name give them a brick that they can add to the tower. Keep calling names until you have used all the bricks up. The last child to put a brick on the tower is allowed to topple the tower over.
Helpful hint	Rather than going around in a circle, call out children's names in a random order so that they have to wait and listen for their name.
Making it harder	Increase the pace of the game and shorten the amount of time between names. As well as using the children's names, you can call out a colour with each name. That child then needs to select the correct colour brick.

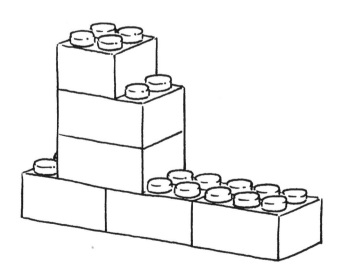

Look at Me

Expected Time Quick	**Resources needed** None	
Challenge level Beginner		

Aim	For children to make eye contact with other group members and respond to a visual cue
Method	Model to the children covering your eyes and count to three. When you get to three, uncover your eyes and look directly at a child in the group. Tell the child who is being looked at to put up their hand and say, 'It's me!' It is now this child's turn to cover their eyes. They count to three and then look directly at another person in the group. Continue this around the group a few times.
Helpful hint	Encourage children to choose a child who has not had a turn so that everyone can join in.

Who is Wearing the Hat?

Expected Time
Quick

Challenge level
Beginner

Resources needed
❖ An interesting hat or other items you can wear, such as glasses, a wig or a mask
❖ Mirror (optional)

Aim	For children to look at another child and answer a simple question
Method	Tell the group that you are going to put the hat on someone. Wait for a moment so that the children are looking and anticipating what will happen. Place the hat on one child's head and ask the group, 'Who is wearing the hat?' The other children must point or say the name of the child who is wearing the hat. Use a mirror so the child with the hat on can look at themselves. The hat could be replaced with other items such as glasses, wig or mask.
Making it harder	Use two different items such as glasses and hat and put them on different children. Ask 'Who has the hat?' This requires children to listen more closely to the question asked.

Find the Sound

Expected Time Quick	**Resources needed** ❖ Noisy toy or other sound-maker, such as a wind-up clock ❖ Cloth (optional)
Challenge level Beginner	

Aim	For children to listen carefully and identify where a sound is coming from
Method	Ask the children to close their eyes. Hide a wind-up toy or a noisy toy somewhere in the room: for example, under a cloth or under the table. Encourage children to listen carefully. Tell the children they can now open their eyes. Ask them to guess where the toy is by pointing or saying the place.
Making it harder	Hide two or more toys at the same time.

Ready, Steady, Go!

Expected Time	**Resources needed**
Quick	Musical instruments or shakers

Challenge level
Beginner

Aim	For children to wait and listen for a word that signals the start of an activity
Method	Give each of the children a musical instrument that they must keep silent. Say 'Ready, steady, go!'. They must wait until they hear 'go!' before they start playing. The children must continue playing until they hear 'stop'.
Helpful hint	Children will naturally want to shake their instruments when they are given them. Try asking them to place the instruments on the table without touching them before the first turn.
Making it harder	One musical instrument is placed in the middle of the group. One child is selected to play. Choose children in random order so they need to listen for their name.

Pass the Squeeze

Expected Time
Quick

Resources needed
None

Challenge level
Beginner

Aim	For children to wait and respond to a tactile cue during a non-verbal activity
Method	Explain that this is a silent game. Group members must all hold hands in a circle. One person is chosen to start the squeeze by gently squeezing the hand of the person next to them, either to the left or right. The squeeze is then passed along the circle in the same direction as it started, left or right. Continue silently until the adult chooses when to stop the squeezes.
Making it harder	Pass a 'squeeze sequence', for example, three or four squeezes in a row. Introduce a 'change direction' cue, which is two squeezes in a row.

Attention & Listening

Pass the Rhythm

Expected Time
Quick

Resources needed
Shakers (optional)

Challenge level
Beginner

Aim	For children to take turns and copy a sequence of sounds
Method	Start by making up a rhythm using handclaps or a musical shaker. Perform the rhythm to the group, then explain that you are passing it on to the next person. This child has to copy the same beats to make the rhythm. They then pass it on and this continues around the group. Encourage children to listen and look carefully so they copy the rhythm correctly.
Making it easier	All group members copy the same rhythm together. Break the rhythm down and count how many beats there are. Those who have difficulties remembering the rhythm may find it easier to count in their head when it is their turn.

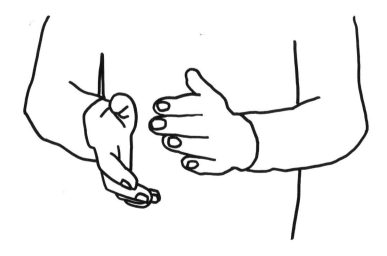

Throw the Finger

Expected Time
Quick

Resources needed
None

Challenge level
Beginner

Aim	For children to maintain eye contact and take turns during a visual activity
Method	Start by holding up your index finger. Mime throwing the finger to another person using your other hand. The children must look carefully to see if the finger is coming to them. If it has been thrown to them, they can mime catching it. Remind the children to keep looking because if they are not looking they may miss their turn at catching it. The person who catches the finger then passes it on to another person in the same way.

Tunnel Game

Expected Time	**Resources needed**
Mid-length	❖ Expanding tunnel toy; or make a pretend tunnel by placing two or more chairs next to each other, creating a space for children to crawl underneath.
Challenge level	❖ 'Stop and go' sign (optional)
Beginner	

Aim	For children to wait for a visual cue or a verbal command to start moving
Method	Prepare the tunnel (see Resources needed). Ask children to line up to take turns at crawling through. Tell the children to wait and listen carefully for you to say 'Go!', they can only go through the tunnel when they hear 'Go'.
Making it easier	Use a red 'Stop' and a green 'Go' sign. The children must wait until the sign shows 'Go' before they crawl through.
Making it harder	Increase the amount of time that you make the children wait – this challenges them to maintain attention and remain still.

Name Race

Aim	For children to listen and respond to a one word instruction
Method	Everyone sits in a circle. Start by calling out two children's names at a time. The two children whose names are called must jump up, run around the group, then come back and sit in their places. Keep repeating this with different combinations of children's names. Occasionally call out 'Everyone!', which means that the whole group has to get up and run around the circle once before sitting back down in their original place.
Helpful hint	Many children with attention and listening difficulties do not respond to instructions that are given to 'everyone'. It is worth having a discussion before you start about what the word 'everyone' actually means. You may be surprised that some children do not think it applies to them at all. After practising appropriate responses to 'everyone' in group sessions, talk to their class teachers so that the children can gain practice and support in the classroom as well.

Attention & Listening

Fruit Salad

<table>
<tr><td>Expected Time
Mid-length</td><td>Resources needed
Toy fruits or pictures of different fruit</td></tr>
</table>

Challenge level
Beginner

Aim	For children to listen and respond to a one word instruction
Method	Everyone sits in a circle and each child is given a picture of a fruit or a toy fruit. Ask each child to say the name of their fruit to ensure they are familiar with the vocabulary. Start the game by calling out two fruits at a time, for example, 'orange and strawberry'. The two children who have those fruits must jump up, run around the circle, and then come back and sit in their places. Keep repeating this with different combinations of fruits. Occasionally call out 'Fruit salad!', which means that all the children have to run around the circle once before sitting back in their original place.
Making it harder	Tell children the name of their fruit but do not give them an object or picture of it. In this version the children need to remember which fruit they are.

Musical Statues

Resources needed
❖ Stereo or other music player
❖ CD or other music source or
❖ A musical instrument

Aim For children to listen and respond to a change in music

Method Start playing some music and ask the children to dance to it. Explain to the children that when they hear the music stop they must immediately stand very still, like a statue. After playing the music for a short time, stop it abruptly. The children must listen carefully and respond by being still. The last person to be still sits out. This continues until only one person remains.

Attention & Listening

Musical Chairs

Expected Time
Mid-length

Challenge level
Beginner

Resources needed
- ❖ Chairs: one fewer than the total number of children
- ❖ Stereo or other music player or
- ❖ A musical instrument

Aim   For children to listen and respond to a change in music

Method   Place the chairs in a circle so that they are facing outwards. Start playing some music and ask the children to walk around the chairs whilst the music plays. Explain to the children that when they hear the music stop they must immediately find a chair and sit down. After playing the music for a short time, stop it abruptly. The children must listen carefully and respond by sitting down. The person who does not find a chair sits out. Each time take one chair away, so there is always one less chair than the total number of children. This continues until only one person remains.

Match the Sound

Expected Time
Mid-length

Challenge level
Beginner

Resources needed
- ❖ Pictures of animals or objects that make sounds (e.g., clock, kettle, whistle, bell)
- ❖ Sound recording of the noises these things make (optional) or
- ❖ Musical instruments and matching pictures

Aim	For children to make an association between a sound that they hear and a matching picture
Method	Place pictures of the chosen objects or animals in the middle of the table. Make the sound or play a recording of one of the objects. The children must listen carefully. One child is chosen to identify which picture matches the sound. Start with two or three pictures and gradually increase the number of choices.
	Instead of making the noises yourself you can purchase a 'Guess the sound' game that comes with a CD and pictures.
	This game can also be played with musical instruments. Place pictures of the instruments on the table, and play the instrument under the table so the children cannot see which one is being played. They must then identify the matching instrument from the pictures.
Making it harder	Increase the number of pictures to choose from.
	Choose less familiar objects that make the sounds.

Attention & Listening

Outdoor Sounds

Expected Time Quick	**Resources needed** None
Challenge level Intermediate	

Aim	For children to listen carefully and identify the location of a sound
Method	Explain to the group that they will need to listen carefully to sounds they can hear outdoors. You could move the group outside to play this game so that they can focus better on outdoor sounds. Ask the group to close their eyes. Choose one child and ask them to name a sound they can hear (e.g., a car alarm). Keeping their eyes closed, the rest of the group have to point in the direction they think that sound is coming from. Count to three and ask everyone to open their eyes. See if everyone is pointing in the same direction. Continue playing with a new child being chosen to name a sound each time.

Pass the Whisper

Expected Time
Quick

Resources needed
None

Challenge level
Intermediate

Aim	For children to listen to and repeat a spoken sentence
Method	Choose a special word or short sentence to say and whisper it into the ear of one child. This child then whispers it to the next person until the last person receives it. The last person has to say aloud what the whispered message was.
Making it easier	Repeat the whispered sentence if requested.
Making it harder	Make longer sentences and use less familiar words.

Sounds Around You

Attention & Listening

Expected Time Mid-length	**Resources needed** None

Challenge level
Intermediate

Aim	For children to listen and identify environmental sounds that they have heard
Method	Ask everyone to closes their eyes for a short time (20 seconds to 1 minute). They must then listen carefully to sounds in the environment around them. Encourage the children to stay silent during this activity. After the agreed time, tell the children to open their eyes and report back on what they have heard: for example, a car horn, another class singing, a dog barking.
Making it harder	Increase the length of time that the group listens for sounds.

Pass the Imaginary Object

Expected Time	Resources needed
Mid-length	Box wrapped in coloured paper

Challenge level
Intermediate

Aim For children to look at and interpret others' actions

Method One person is chosen to think of an imaginary object, which will be inside a box. Without saying what it is, they mime taking it out of the box. The imaginary object is then passed around the group. Encourage the children to look carefully at how the person who takes the object out of the box holds it, so that they can judge the object's shape, size and weight. After everyone has passed the object the children must guess what it was. Repeat this for each group member until everyone has had a turn at thinking of an object.

Kim's Game

Expected Time Mid-length	**Resources needed** ❖ Six to ten familiar objects ❖ Tray to place the objects on ❖ Piece of cloth large enough to cover the tray
Challenge level Intermediate	

Aim	For children to look and use visual memory to identify a missing object
Method	Start by placing six objects out on a tray. Pick up each object and ask the children to name it. Tell them to look carefully at all the objects because in a few moments they will need to remember what is on the tray. Encourage the group to look at the objects for about ten seconds. Cover the objects with a cloth and take the tray away. Without letting the children see, reach under the cloth and take one object away. Place the tray back on the table and remove the cloth. Ask the group to look and guess which object has been removed.
Helpful hint	Encourage the children to put their hand up once they know which object is missing. This way the children who need more time to think do not miss out. Talk about how the children might remember the objects, such as repeating the names in their mind or imagining them.
Making it harder	As well as removing one object, move the remaining objects around.

Handout 4
Attention & Listening in the Classroom

Children who have difficulties with attention and listening can miss out on a lot of important information in the classroom. Here are some suggestions of ways to support children with these difficulties to access learning opportunities.

1 Use the group rules of 'good sitting', 'good looking', 'good listening', 'wait for your turn' as active listening prompts in the classroom (see Resources, Group Rules Cards, p. 198). Display the rules with their symbols on the wall in the classroom and point or refer to them regularly. Praise children who are showing positive behaviour, rather than only drawing attention to them when they are not listening.

2 Before giving instructions, say the child's name or use a physical prompt: for example, gently touch the child's arm to remind them to look at you.

3 Make sure that children who have difficulties with listening and maintaining attention are sitting near to the teacher and are free from distractions.

4 Keep instructions short and chunk longer sections of information into smaller parts, with pauses in between.

5 Use lots of multi-sensory information prompts, such as real objects, toys, photos, pictures, symbols, music, instruments and information technology.

Understanding & Auditory Memory

Spoken language is the main way in which teaching is delivered in the classroom. Children need to be able to listen to what is said, but they also need to understand the meaning. Many children with poor understanding do not have strategies to support themselves and so, as well as developing their skills in understanding, it is useful to teach children what to do when they do not understand.

To help children to understand and remember, encourage them to look at other group members as they are speaking. When playing games involving instructions, encourage children to listen carefully to all the words, repeat them to themselves, and then visualise what they need to do.

Difficulties with understanding may be a reason for some children's challenging behaviour. When managing challenging behaviour it is important to consider the child's ability to understand spoken language, and whether they have misinterpreted or misunderstood what to do. It is easy to overlook difficulties with understanding when a child's behaviour has become difficult.

Indicators of Difficulty with Understanding & Auditory Memory

Children who have difficulties with understanding and auditory memory may display some of these features:

❖ not knowing what to do when instructions have been given, resulting in difficulty with getting started on a task;

❖ not being able to repeat back instructions or explain what they need to do;

❖ appearing passive and reluctant to participate or, alternatively, being off-task and disruptive;

❖ difficulties learning new vocabulary and needing a word to be repeated many times before it is learnt;

❖ needing information to be simplified to be fully understood;

❖ giving responses that are not related to the question or to the topic being discussed;

❖ appearing confused and not knowing what to do when asked;

❖ copying other children's work or following their actions when they are supposed to be working independently; and

❖ showing significant difficulty with learning times tables, days of the week or telephone numbers.

Understanding & Auditory Memory Targets

1 To make visual associations in order to match objects to pictures or symbols

2 To understand instructions with one or two key words containing nouns

3 To understand a single key word instructions containing position concepts

4 To understand instructions with two key words, containing nouns and verbs

5 To recall the order that events happened

6 To recall a series of words

7 To understand concepts of colour, size and position in instructions with two key words

8 To understand and follow a sequence of instructions with two parts

9 To recall a given word or phrase

10 To understand instructions with three or four key words, containing nouns, verbs and adjectives

11 To follow instructions using directional language (e.g. at the top, left, middle)

12 To understand complex instructions containing the concepts of order (e.g. before/after) and condition (e.g., if/when)

Photo Match

Expected Time
Mid-length

Challenge level
Beginner

Resources needed
- ❖ Real objects or toys of familiar everyday items: for example, toothbrush, teddy, watch, pencil
- ❖ Clear photos of the similar items. These could be: real photographs, commercially available picture cards, or pictures cut out of magazines or catalogues.

Aim	To identify and match a real object to a photograph of that type of object
Method	Place all of the photos in front of the children, saying the name of each one as it is placed down. Model putting the one object on its matching photo (e.g., toy teddy on photo of the teddy), and then give the child a choice of objects to then match with another photo.
Making it easier	Have less choice of objects and photos.
Making it harder	Have more choice of objects and photos.

Symbol Match

Expected Time Mid-length	**Resources needed**
Challenge level Beginner	❖ Real objects or toys of familiar everyday items: for example, toothbrush, teddy, watch, pencil ❖ Matching symbols or pictures of these types of objects. Use commercially available symbol-making computer programmes, or images gathered from the internet.

Aim	To identify and match a real object to a symbol or drawing of that type of object
Method	Place each of the symbols in front of the children, naming each one as it is placed down. Model putting one object on its matching symbol. Then give the first child a choice of objects to then match with other symbols.
Making it easier	Have less choice of objects and symbols
Making it harder	Have more choice of objects and symbols.

Show Me!

Expected Time
Quick

Challenge level
Beginner

Resources needed
❖ A mixture of familiar objects or
❖ A mixture of familiar pictures

Aim	To understand instructions with one key word
Method	Lay out the objects or pictures in front of the children. Ask each child in turn to point to one of the objects, saying, 'Show me the [name of object]'. If a child points to a different object or picture, say, 'Good try, not that one', and repeat the instruction.
Making it easier	Use a Makaton® sign (or similar) when saying the name of the object.
Making it harder	Increase the number of objects, pictures, or symbols to choose from. Ask the child to find two items.

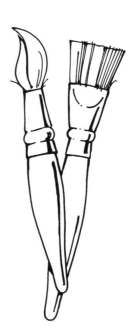

'Find This Many ...'

Expected Time	**Resources needed**
Quick	A range of small toys or objects

Challenge level
Beginner

Aim

To understand and respond to short instructions

Method

Place objects on the table. Decide on the number of objects that you want the child to find and hold up that many fingers. For instance, if you want the child to find two objects, hold up two fingers. Give each child a turn to listen to an instruction: for example, 'Find the car and the scissors.'

Making it harder

Increase the number of objects to find.

Place the objects further away so the child needs to move to get the objects. This encourages them to hold the instruction in their memory for longer.

Do not show the number on your fingers. Instead, encourage the children to listen and hold up their fingers when they hear how many objects you say.

Posting Game

Expected Time
Mid-length

Challenge level
Beginner

Resources needed
❖ Toy postbox: make one out of an old shoe or gift box, wrap with wrapping paper and cut out a posting hole.
❖ Pictures or symbols of common familiar objects

Aim	To understand instructions with one key word
Method	Place a range of pictures of common objects in front of the children. Choose a child to start and ask them to listen and post the picture of the words that you say. For example, 'Michael, post the [say key word].'
Making it easier	Use a Makaton® sign (or similar) when saying the name of the object. Model to the child how to put the correct item into the postbox. Then ask them to have another turn and do the same.
Making it harder	Make the goal of understanding and following instructions more complex by using two key words and asking the child to post two items, for example, 'Post the drink and the car.' Use pictures of people doing actions, for example, 'Post the man who is running.'

Hungry Puppet

Expected Time
Mid-length

Challenge level
Beginner

Resources needed
❖ Puppet, teddy or doll
❖ A mixture of toy food items, or pictures of different foods

Aim	To understand instructions with one key word
Method	Explain that the puppet is very hungry and that the children need to help to feed him. Each child in turn listens to your instruction to feed the puppet an item of food. For example, 'Kevin, feed the puppet an orange.'
Making it easier	Use a Makaton sign (or similar) when saying the name of the food to support the children's understanding. Model giving the correct item to the puppet and ask the child to repeat.
Making it harder	Make the goal of understanding and following instructions more complex by using two key words and introducing a second puppet or toy. Give instructions that specify the food and which toy is to be fed. For example, 'Feed the sandwich to the lion.'

Big Box

Expected Time
Mid-length

Resources needed
A very large cardboard box

Challenge level
Beginner

Aim	To understand instructions that use prepositions (position words)
Method	Place the big box in the centre of the circle. Explain to the group that they will be moving around the big box and that they need to listen carefully to hear where to go. Each child has a turn at listening to an instruction that includes a preposition. For example, say, 'Ellie, get *under* the box.' Or a popular one, 'Get *in* the box.'

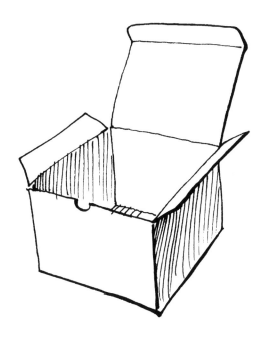

Simon Says

Expected Time
Mid-length

Resources needed
None

Challenge level
Beginner

Aim	For children to listen to simple instructions and copy movements
Method	Ask the children to stand up. Give simple instructions to the whole group, beginning with the words 'Simon says', for example, 'Simon says touch your toes.' Model doing the actions (e.g., touching your toes) each time an instruction is given. The children should only carry out the action if the words 'Simon says' are used. Occasionally give an instruction that does not start with 'Simon says'. If someone moves when 'Simon says' was not said, they have to miss a turn.
Variation	Use your own name, for example, 'Michelle says [say action to be performed].'
Making it harder	Do not continue to model the actions. Give the instructions only, so that the children have to listen carefully to the instructions.

Bossy Teddy

Expected Time Mid-length	**Resources needed** Teddy bear
Challenge level Beginner	

Aim	For children to follow simple verbal instructions to perform an action
Method	Introduce the teddy bear to the children and explain that he is called Bossy Teddy because he likes to tell children what to do. Each child has a turn at listening to Bossy Teddy giving them an instruction to carry out. Use a funny voice and hold up the teddy when giving the instructions. Use the phrase 'Bossy Teddy says', and then tell the child to perform a simple action, such as pointing to a body part or moving around the room, for example: 'Bossy Teddy says touch your nose', and 'Bossy Teddy says run to the door.' Continue around the group until each child has had one or two turns.
Making it easier	Prepare visual prompt cards with symbols or drawings linked to the instructions, for example, if Bossy Teddy says 'run to the door', show a picture of a boy running towards a door.
Making it harder	Ask the children to perform two actions, for example, 'Bossy Teddy says rub your tummy then jump up and down.'

Obstacle Course

Expected Time
Mid-length

Challenge level
Beginner

Resources needed
❖ A range of objects that can be obstacles, such as a hoop, a box, a chair, a bin and a box
❖ Space to move around: a school hall or large classroom is ideal for this activity.

Aim	For children to follow instructions that include nouns (naming words), verbs (action words) and prepositions (position words)
Method	Place various objects around the room, for example, a hoop, a box, a chair, a bin, and a box. Decide which prepositions you want to target (e.g., in, on, under, behind, through, around, over, in front). It may be easier to focus on only a few at a time. Ask each child in turn to follow an instruction, for example, 'Jump *over* the box.'
Making it harder	Build up the number of instructions so that the children have to follow a sequence of instructions, for example: ❖ 'Jump *over* the box and crawl *through* the hoop.' ❖ 'Run *around* the hoop and then sit *on* the bin.'

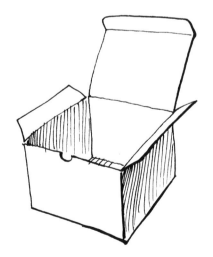

Who Can You Find?

Expected Time Quick	**Resources needed** ❖ A busy picture with lots of different things happening in it ❖ Books like *Where's Wally?* are particularly useful and usually popular, but they can be tricky!
Challenge level Beginner	

Aim	For children to understand simple instructions relating to a picture
Method	Place an enlarged busy picture in the middle of the group, or give each group member their own copy to look at. Each child in turn is asked to find a particular person who is doing an action, for example: 'Find the boy who is singing', and 'Find the man who is sweeping.'
Making it harder	This could also be played to develop understanding of 'wh' questions, for example: '*Who* is wearing green?'; '*What* is on the signpost?'; and '*Where* is the big red car?' A prompt sheet with symbols of the different 'wh' questions will be useful for this. An example is provided in the Resources section (see Question Prompts, p. 214).

Whisper the Instruction

Expected Time
Mid-length

Resources needed
A mixture of everyday objects and toys

Challenge level
Beginner

Aim	For children to listen to, repeat and follow an instruction
Method	Whisper a simple instruction to do an action to the first child, for example, 'Touch your nose', or 'Put the glove in the bag.' The child must whisper it to the second person and it is then passed around the group. The last child must carry out the instruction. The group watches what the last person does and then you can confirm whether or not the action was the same as the instruction you whispered. Continue playing, allowing the children to take turns at thinking of the instruction to give.
Making it easier	Whisper the instruction to just one child. They must repeat what they heard out loud and then follow the instruction.

What Did We Do?

Expected Time Quick	**Resources needed** None

Challenge level Beginner

Aim	For children to recall and describe what they have done in the group session that day
Method	At the end of a group session ask the children to recall the activities they have done in that session. Each child has a turn at remembering one activity.
Helpful hint	If you used a visual timetable, cover it up during this activity.
Making it easier	Show symbols from the visual timetable as prompts for recall.
Making it harder	Ask the children to say in which order the activities were completed.

'I Went Shopping'

Expected Time Mid-length	**Resources needed** None

Challenge level Intermediate

Aim	To use a memory strategy to recall a series of words
Method	Start by naming an object that you would buy in a shop, using the phrase, 'I went shopping and I bought [say the name of an object].' For example, 'I went shopping and I bought an apple.' The turn moves to a child who has to repeat what was just said and then add another item. Continue doing this by going on to the next child, making a list of things that can be bought at the shops. For example, 'I went shopping and I bought an apple, some chocolate and a magazine.' And so it continues with each child recalling what others have said before adding an item of their own.
	You can use different variations, such as: 'I went on holiday and in my suitcase I put …'
	❖ 'I made a sandwich and in it I put …'
	❖ 'I made a horrible sandwich and in it I put [spiders, worms, mud, etc.]'
	❖ 'I went to a sports shop and I bought …'
	❖ 'I went to the fruit shop and I bought …'
	❖ 'I went to the beach and I saw …'
Making it easier	Prompt children who are having difficulty remembering with a description of the item (e.g., if the item was 'butter', you could give them a hint, saying, 'You spread it on your toast').
	Prompt children by giving the first sound of the word (e.g., 'It starts with "b"').
Making it harder	Go around the group a second time, so that everyone adds another item.

Change Places

Expected Time
Quick

Resources needed
None

Challenge level
Intermediate

Aim	For children to respond to instructions that relate to themselves
Method	Call out instructions to the group, for example, 'Change places if you have a brother', or 'Change places if you are wearing blue.' The children must listen carefully and stand up and change places if the instruction applies to them.
Helpful hint	This game involves lots of children moving around at the same time, so clear away any obstacles and ensure that there is space for the children to move from their place. This can be a useful game to play if you think that a child is seated next to someone unsuitable (e.g., someone who distracts them). Keep getting them to move around until the children are in positions that will work best.

Guess Who It Is

Expected Time Mid-length	**Resources needed** None

Challenge level Intermediate

Aim	For children to listen and respond to instructions that relate to themselves
Method	Ask the children to all stand up. Decide which child you are going to describe and tell the group that you have chosen someone, but they have to guess who it is. Say a sentence that describes one or more members of the group, for example, 'This person has brown hair.' Explain that if the sentence applies to them then they must stay standing. If it does not apply to them they must sit down. So, for this example, all the children with black, blonde or red hair would sit down.

Keep giving descriptions until there is only one person left. |
Helpful hint	This game works best when you have a larger group of children. It also works well with a whole class of children.
Making it easier	If children sit down when they should have remained standing, repeat the sentence back to them and ask everyone to check what they heard. It may be necessary to explain what they have to do, for example, 'This person has brown hair. If you have brown hair stay standing. If your hair is a different colour, sit down.'
Making it harder	Introduce prepositions into the sentences, for example, 'This person is standing *beside* a wall.' Pronouns could also be used to add detail and complexity, for example, '*He* is wearing white.'

Listen for the Actions

Expected Time
Quick

Resources needed
None

Challenge level
Intermediate

Aim	To follow a sequence of instructions to perform simple actions
Method	Explain to the group that you will be giving them instructions to carry out a series of actions in order. Then give instructions to the whole group to carry out around three actions. Include sequential language, such as 'first', 'next', 'then', and 'finally'. For example, 'First clap your hands, then touch your nose and, finally, rub your tummy.'
Helpful hint	Remind the children to wait until the whole instruction has been given before they start moving.
Making it easier	Give one action only.

Special Sentence

Expected Time Quick	**Resources needed** None

Challenge level Intermediate

Aim	To remember a short phrase with a time delay
Method	Choose a phrase at the beginning of the group (e.g., 'green eggs and ham') and say it aloud together. Ask the pupils if they can recall it twice over the duration of the session. Ask them to recall it at the end of the session.
Making it easier	Use an object or symbol associated with the phrase: for example, for the phrase 'green eggs and ham', show the children an egg. Show the group the egg each time they are asked to recall the phrase.
Making it harder	Only recall the phrase once, at the end of the group.

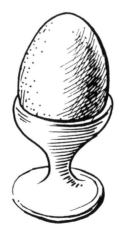

Special Names

Expected Time	Resources needed
Quick	None

Challenge level
Intermediate

Aim	To think of an adjective that begins with the same sound as their name
	To recall other group members' descriptive name
Method	All group members have a turn at making up a special name for themselves by choosing a word that begins with the same sound as their name, for example, 'My name is Clever Chloe.' Go around the group and each child must try to remember what others' special names were.
Making it harder	Play an activity in between choosing the names and recalling each other's special names. This introduces a delay, which is more challenging on children's memory.

Understanding & Auditory Memory

Special Animal

Expected Time
Quick

Resources needed
None

Challenge level
Intermediate

Aim	For children to visualise and be able to recall a verbally described object
Method	At the start of the group decide on an animal and tell the children what it is. Tell them to visualise the animal by making a picture in their head. Ask each child a question about the animal, telling them to imagine what it is like, for example: 'What is it doing?'; 'What is it eating?'; or 'What colour is it?' Ask all of the children to visualise that image and make a picture in their heads. At the end of the session ask the group to try to remember the visual image of their animal. Ask each child to describe something they can remember about the animal.
Helpful hint	Play this game at start of the session, so that there are a few activities in between the visualisation and the recall.
Making it easier	Ask the group to visualise just one feature of the animal, for example, what action the animal is doing.
Making it harder	Call on just one child to recall the visual image at the end of the group.

Listen and Do

Expected Time Mid-length	**Resources needed** 8–10 familiar objects. Choose objects that things can go in, on, under or behind (e.g., a box, a cup, a plate, a bag) and some other smaller objects (e.g., a dice, a pen).
Challenge level Intermediate	

Aim	To follow instructions of increasing length and complexity
Method	Place the objects on the table in front of the group. Each child has a turn to listen and do and they must listen carefully to instructions to move an object to a specific place. For example, 'Put the brush *on* the plate.'
Helpful hint	Before starting the activity decide on the number of key words you are aiming for the children to understand and remember. For example, 'Put the *brush on* the *plate*' is a three keyword instruction.
Making it easier	Reinforce understanding of the position words ('in', 'on', 'under' etc.) by using a Makaton® sign or similar.
Making it harder	It is important that children have plenty of success so do not make the activity harder too early. Once the children are consistently getting their actions right, you can make the instructions more difficult by: ❖ increasing the length of the sentence (e.g., 'Put the big black pen under the red box') ❖ introducing choices (e.g., 'Put the dice or the spoon under the bag') ❖ combining two requests (e.g., 'Put the cup on the box and then turn the plate over')

Barrier Game

Expected Time
Lengthy

Challenge level
Advanced

Resources needed

❖ Free standing barriers. Ring binders or large books standing up on their bottom edge work well.

❖ Sets of small matching objects or pictures, such as toy animals, toy bricks of varying colours, or other small objects (enough for each child in the group).

❖ A 'base picture' for each child. A grid with different colours or pictures within each square works well. A line drawing of a large picture scene could also be used.

Aim	For children to listen and follow a series of instructions containing three or four key words
Method	Give each child a base picture and an identical set of small objects or pictures. Place a barrier between the children so they cannot see each other's materials. One child is the 'speaker' and the others are the 'listeners'. The speaker must give instructions to the others to move their objects around, for example, 'Put the butterfly on the red square', or 'Put the big car on the blue door.'
	Encourage the listeners to say if they have not understood the instruction by asking, 'What did you say?', or 'Please say that again.' Once the instructions have all been given the barrier is removed and children compare their objects and pictures to see if they match. Swap roles so that there is a new 'speaker'.
Making it easier	Give each child a container, like a box or a cup. The speaker gives instructions containing prepositions, such as 'Put the cow *in* the box', or 'Put the brick *under* the box.'
Making it harder	Increase the number of objects to choose from. Give longer instructions that contain two parts, or have objects which are more similar and so need closer description, like big and small versions of the same objects or the same objects in different colours.

Colouring Game

Expected Time
Lengthy

Challenge level
Advanced

Resources needed

❖ Identical picture scenes for each child. Worksheets with clear picture scenes are available in commercial packs of barrier games. Worksheets from other curriculum books like maths or science workbooks may also be appropriate. Also try searching for scenes on the internet or in colouring books. There is an example of a worksheet for this in the Resources section (see Worksheet for Colouring Game, p. 208).

❖ A set of three or four colouring pencils for each child. Each set needs to contain the same colours.

Aim	To follow specific instructions with two to four key words, relating to a picture scene
Method	Give each child a set of the same coloured pencils and a copy of the same worksheet. Give an instruction to the group, for example, 'Colour the first smiley face green', or 'Colour the last star red'. Ask the children to compare their worksheets at the end to check that they were all listening carefully.
Helpful hint	Discuss strategies the children can use if they do not understand. Encourage them to ask for specific help, for example, 'Can you please say that again?', or 'I didn't hear which colour to use.'
	Use a memory strategy prompt sheet, like the one in the Resources section (see Memory Strategy, p. 215).
Making it easier	Give simpler and shorter instructions. Not specifying which colour to use will make the instruction shorter and easier to remember.
Making it harder	Give longer and more complex instructions, for example, 'Colour the flower that's beside the tallest tree purple.'
	Give a sequence of instructions, for example, 'Colour the first star green and the third square yellow.'

Barrier Game Sequence

Expected Time
Lengthy

Challenge level
Advanced

Resources needed
❖ Free standing barriers. Ring binders or large books standing on their bottom edge work well.
❖ Matching sets of picture cards, one set for each child.

Aim	For children to follow sequential instructions
Method	Sit children in pairs at a table with a barrier between them. Give each child a set of the same pictures so that they each have a complete set. One child chooses some pictures, puts them in a row on the table, and describes the order they have put them in to the other person. For example, 'I'm putting down a seed, a leaf, a branch and then the flowers.' The other child must choose the same pictures and place them on the table in the same order to make an exact copy. Make sure that the child listening waits until the instruction has finished before they start, otherwise they are not using their memory. The barrier is then lifted and they can check if they have correctly matched the sequence.
Making it easier	Tell the children to make a sequence with fewer pictures.

Barrier Game Pizzas

Expected Time
Lengthy

Challenge level
Advanced

Resources needed
- ❖ Free standing barriers. Ring binders or large books standing on their bottom edge work well.
- ❖ A 'pizza base' for each child. Use a round circle drawn on paper to represent this.
- ❖ Sets of 'pizza toppings': use pictures of foods such as onions, tomatoes, salami, ham, pineapple, and cheese.

Aim	For children to listen and follow a series of instructions containing directional language
Method	Give each child a pizza base and an identical set of pizza toppings. Place a barrier between the children so they cannot see each other's pizza. One child is the 'speaker' and the others are the 'listeners'. The speaker must give instructions to the others to add toppings to their pizza, in a specific location, for example, 'Put some onions in the middle of the pizza', or 'Put some salami around the edges.' Encourage the listeners to say if they have not understood the instruction by asking, 'What did you say?', or 'Please say that again.' Once all of the toppings have been added, remove the barrier and children can compare their pizzas to see if they match. Swap roles so that there is a new 'speaker'.
Helpful hint	You could make this into a really fun and practical cooking activity by using real pizza bases and toppings. It could also work well to make sandwiches or other foods.
Making it harder	Increase the number of objects to choose from. Give longer instructions that contain two parts. Or have toppings which are quite similar and so need closer description, like red and green peppers, or big and small mushrooms.

Tricky Simon Says

Expected Time
Mid-length

Resources needed
None

Challenge level
Advanced

Aim	For children to follow complex instructions
Method	Ask the children to stand up. Give detailed instructions to the whole group, beginning with the words 'Simon says'. For example, 'Simon says before you touch your head clap your hands.' Make this tricky by using more complicated grammar and word order in the instructions, for example, 'If there's a boy in our group called Henry, hop on one leg.' The children should only carry out the actions if the words 'Simon says' are used. Occasionally give an instruction that does not start with 'Simon says'. If someone moves when 'Simon says' was not spoken, they have to miss a turn.
Making it harder	Use language that incorporates sequence words (e.g., 'before', 'after'), less common body parts (e.g., wrist, thigh, knuckle, ankle) and grammatical structures such as 'if', 'when' or 'instead of'.

Listen and Draw

Expected Time
Lengthy

Challenge level
Advanced

Resources needed
❖ Blank pieces of paper and pencils for each child.
❖ List of instructions to create a picture. There is an example of one in the Resources section (see Instructions for Listen and Draw, p. 211). Alternatively, create your own, using this as a basis.

Aim	For children to follow complex instructions to complete a task
Method	Place a barrier like a book or a folder between each child, and also between you and the children. This encourages them not to look at each other's papers. Read out instructions to create a picture slowly, waiting for each child to follow the instruction before moving on to the next one. The group leader also draws the picture, so there is a 'correct' picture at the end to look at. Remove the barriers and compare drawings at the end. Talk about anyone who had a different picture. Ask the children to think what could have helped them to draw the right picture.
Helpful hint	Discuss strategies the children can use if they do not understand. Encourage them to ask for specific help, for example, 'Can you please say that again?', or 'I didn't hear where to draw the circle.' Use a memory strategy prompt sheet, like the one in the Resources section of this book (see Memory Strategy, p. 215).
Making it easier	Compare drawings after each instruction to check that everyone has understood.

Understanding & Auditory Memory in the Classroom

As well as practising the understanding and auditory memory strategies in small groups, it is important that children receive support in the classroom. Difficulties with understanding are a challenge to resolve, so classroom strategies are crucial. These suggestions will help to supporting children's understanding and memory in the classroom environment.

1 Keep instructions short and use simple language structures. Try not to put too much information in each sentence. Try to make important instructions very short.

2 When giving long and detailed verbal information to a class, try to summarise the main points in short, punchy phrases. For example, 'Three things happened in this passage. First the old man became ill. Then Ronald was sent to find the doctor. Finally Ronald got lost on his way to find the doctor.'

3 Use visual information such as visual timetables, objects, photos, pictures and symbols to support your spoken language. Visuals are more permanent than spoken words and so children can focus on them even if they did not understand fully what was said.

4 Encourage children to visualise the main part of an instruction, which should help them to follow it more accurately and quickly. For example, 'I want you to picture what your history book looks like. Picture where it is. Now go and get your history book.'

5 Check that children have understood by asking them to repeat back the instructions they have heard in their own words.

6 Give children plenty of time to process verbal information and instructions. Observe how long it takes an individual child to respond. Some children need extra processing time, particularly in response to questions.

7 Give children prompts to use 'thinking time' before they rush to answer a question.

8 Encourage children to indicate when they have not understood something. This helps them to get all the information they need, rather than pretending that they know what to do. Discuss examples of ways they can say they have not understood, such as 'I don't know what to do', or 'I didn't hear you.' Encourage them to become more specific with these statements, such as 'I've got my diary, but what do I need to write in it?'

Expressive Language

Spoken language is the main way in which children express themselves. They use their expressive language to get their needs met, to build social relationships and to facilitate their own learning by asking questions. Developing spoken language, including using words in sentences and awareness and use of grammar, also helps to develop children's literacy skills and written expression.

Specific activities to develop the words children use are in the next section, 'Vocabulary, concepts and word finding'. This 'Expressive language' section focuses on children's use of grammatical structures within words and sentences.

Indicators of Difficulty with Expressive Language

Children who have difficulties with expressive language may display these features:

❖ using only single words or a few words joined together;

❖ using simplistic or very short sentences;

❖ using grammatical structures more typical of a younger child;

❖ difficulties with specific grammatical forms such as past tense markers, pronouns, or plurals; and

❖ the child's sentences have a jumbled word order.

Expressive Language Targets

1 To use single words or two-word phrases containing nouns and verbs

2 To use phrases or instructions with two key words, containing nouns, and verbs

3 To use concept words relating to colour, size and position

4 To give a sequence of instructions with two parts

5 To use phrases or instructions with three key words, containing nouns, verbs and adjectives

6 To give a description of an object

7 To use pronouns 'he', 'she' and 'they'

8 To describe an action using '-ing' verbs and auxiliary verbs 'is'/'are'

9 To ask 'wh' questions

10 To use regular plurals

11 To use possessive pronouns

12 To describe events that have happened in the past, using regular past tense

13 To describe an event or story in a sequence

14 To use irregular plurals

15 To give complex instructions using directional language (e.g. at the top, left)

16 To give complex instructions using concepts of order (e.g. before, after) and condition (e.g. if, when)

17 To describe events that have happened in the past, using irregular past tense

18 To use long and complex sentences and check that they make sense

Special note: Using Understanding & Auditory Memory Activities as Expressive Language Activities

Many of the activities that are described in the 'Understanding & Auditory Memory' section of this book can be used as expressive language activities too. Just ask the child to take on the role of the speaker rather than listener. When doing this, ensure that the child has had opportunities to hear what they need to say and how to structure it. They may need to hear an adult use the target language structure from the activity several times before they can use it independently. Prompt the child with the correct grammatical form by saying, 'You need to say it like this', and model it to them again.

The following 'Understanding & Auditory Memory' activities can also be used to target expressive language:

- ❖ Posting Game (see p. 57)
- ❖ Hungry Puppet (see p. 58)
- ❖ Big Box (see p. 59)
- ❖ Simon Says (see p. 60)
- ❖ Bossy Teddy (see p. 61)
- ❖ Obstacle Course (see p. 62)
- ❖ Who Can You Find? (see p. 63)
- ❖ Whisper the Instruction (see p. 64)
- ❖ Change Places (see p. 67)

- ❖ Guess Who It Is (see p. 68)
- ❖ Listen for the Actions (see p.69)
- ❖ Listen and Do (see p. 73)
- ❖ Barrier Game (see p. 74)
- ❖ Colouring Game (see p. 75)
- ❖ Barrier Game Sequence (see p. 76)
- ❖ Barrier Game Pizzas (see p. 77)
- ❖ Tricky Simon Says (see p. 78)
- ❖ Listen and Draw (see p. 79)

What's in the Bag?

Expected Time
Quick

Challenge level
Beginner

Resources needed
❖ Opaque bag
❖ Small common and familiar objects or toys

Aim	For children to be able to describe common objects using 1–2 key words
Method	Fill an opaque bag with objects from different word categories, for example, jewellery, stationery, animals, food. Pass the bag around the group. Each child takes a turn at pulling out an object. They must try to name it and say something they know about it. This could be what it does, what it looks like, what it feels like, or what the item is used for. Encourage the children to link words together; for example, if they say 'Blue', say 'Yes, a blue car'.
Making it harder	Ask other children in the group to also describe the same object.

Action Time

Expected Time	**Resources needed**
Quick	❖ Approx. 10 action picture cards
	❖ Opaque bag, box or other container
Challenge level	❖ Soft toys or puppets (optional)
Beginner	

Aim To be able to copy and describe actions using 1–2 key words

Method Place all the action pictures in the bag, box or container, or hold them out in a fan like a deck of cards. The first child takes a card. Tell the child to look at it but not to show the group. They must then mime doing the action that is on the card. Ask the other children in the group to take turns at describing what the actor is doing; for example 'Hopping'. Encourage them to join words together to make a sentence, for example, 'Tom is hopping'. The child with the card then reveals the card so the children can check if they were right.

For an alternative version of this game, use soft toys or puppets and ask the children to make the toy do the action.

Action Pictures

Expected Time	**Resources needed**
Quick	❖ Approx. 10 action picture cards
	❖ Opaque bag, box or other container

Challenge level
Beginner

Aim	To describe action pictures using nouns and verbs in 2 key word phrases
Method	Place all the pictures in the bag, box or container or place them face down on the table for the children to turn over. The children take turns at choosing a picture card and describing what they see the people doing in the picture. For example, 'The man is running.'
Making it easier	Prompt the children to use the right verbs by miming or making a gesture of the action in the picture.
Making it harder	Encourage the children to use a more complicated sentence, including a description of where the person is (e.g., 'The boy is sleeping *on the bed*'), or who or what they are doing the action with or to (e.g., 'The girl is eating *an apple*').

Who Has It?

Expected Time Quick	**Resources needed**
Challenge level Beginner	❖ A picture of a boy and a girl, or a man and a woman. Puppets or dolls could also be used. ❖ Pictures such as clothing, toys, food and accessories that can be people's possessions. ❖ Toy objects could also be used.

Aim To use the pronouns 'he' and 'she' in short sentences

Method Tell the children that you are going to be talking about 'he' and 'she'. Place a picture of a boy and a picture of a girl in the centre of the group. Place a pile of the pictures of their possessions near you. Check the children's understanding of the pronouns by first asking each child to point to which person is 'he' and which refers to 'she'. Ask the first child to choose an object or picture from the pile of possessions. They can choose who to give it to, either the boy or the girl. When they have placed the item with the person, ask them who has that item: if a hat was given to the boy, ask 'Who has the hat?' Encourage the children to answer with the appropriate pronoun, for example, 'he does' or 'she does'. Children will often say 'the boy' or 'the girl' when asked this question. In this case model a choice of the answers, for example, 'Is it "*he* has the hat" or "*she* has the hat?".'

Making it easier Write down the words or use a symbol of 'he' and 'she' and place them next to the boy and girl respectively. Point to the words as needed.

Making it harder Reduce the amount of modelling at the start of the activity.

What's Happening?

Expected Time	Resources needed
Mid-length	❖ Pictures of people doing actions (verb cards)

Expected Time
Mid-length

Challenge level
Beginner

Resources needed
- ❖ Pictures of people doing actions (verb cards)
- ❖ A blank strip of paper or card divided into two parts (sentence strip)
- ❖ Written or printed words that describe the pictures, cut up into noun and verb phrases, e.g. 'the boy' and 'is running'
- ❖ Symbols that depict these phrases could also be used, with the words printed underneath.

Aim   To describe actions using verbs with '-ing' and the auxiliary verbs 'is' and 'are'

Method   Create two piles; one with noun phrases and one with verb phrases. Place the sentence strip on the table as a visual prompt for the children to create a sentence. Choose a picture to show the group and give an example of how to describe what is happening, choosing the right words from the phrase piles to make a full sentence. Place the written words on the sentence strip and say the sentence aloud; for example, 'The boy is running.' Then the children take it in turns to choose a picture from the pile and describe what the person in the picture is doing. Use the sentence strip to prompt the children to include all the words they need by pointing to each section as the child is talking, for example:

Noun phrase – Who?	Verb phrase – What doing?
the boy	is running

If the child leaves out the auxiliary verb ('is' or 'are'), repeat their sentence back to them and ask them to tell you what special word they left out. It can be useful to write the word 'is' on the sentence strip as an extra visual cue to include the auxiliary verb. Continue around the group until each child has a turn at describing one or two pictures.

Who, What, Where?

Expected Time Mid-length	**Resources needed** Pictures of people doing different actions in different places. Cutting out pictures from magazines works well.
Challenge level Intermediate	

Aim To ask a simple 'wh' question

Method Spread out on the table about six pictures of people in different places doing different actions, for example: a man running in the park; a girl swimming in a pool; a girl walking in a wood; a woman driving in a car; a boy kicking a ball in the garden; and a boy eating an ice-cream in the car. Ask one child to choose a picture in their head but to keep it to themselves and not to point to it. The other children in the group have to try to find out which picture they have chosen by asking questions. Take turns at asking questions, such as 'Who is in the picture?', 'Where are they?', and 'What are they doing?' There must be at least three questions asked. When all three questions have been asked and answered the child who asked the last question guesses which picture it is. The child who chose the picture tells the group if they are right or not.

Making it easier Use question word symbols as a visual prompt (see Resources, Question Prompts, p. 214).

Questions About Your News

Expected Time
Mid-length

Challenge level
Intermediate

Resources needed
Prompt sheet with question words and symbols (see Resources, Question Prompts)

Aim	To ask and answer specific 'wh' questions To describe a personal event in a sequence
Method	Start by telling the group some short but interesting news. Leave out some of the specific details. Tell the children to try to find out more information about your news by asking some questions. For example, 'Who did you go there with?', 'When did this happen?', and 'How did you get there?' Provide a prompt sheet with question words and symbols on it to help structure the children's questions. The children then take turns at telling some of their own news to the group (e.g., about their weekend, or a holiday they have been on). The child who told the news must then answer some questions from the group.
Making it harder	Take away the question words and symbol prompt sheet.

In the Hot Seat

Expected Time Mid-length	**Resources needed** A set of cards with question words on them, for example, 'who', 'what', 'where'. The Question prompt sheet with symbols that is provided in the Resources section could be photocopied and cut up for this.
Challenge level Intermediate	

Aim	To ask specific 'wh' questions
Method	Choose one child to be in the hot seat. This means that they will have to answer questions from the rest of the group. Decide on a topic, or ask the children to choose a topic for the game. The group will have to ask the person in the hot seat questions about this topic. Examples could include football, holidays, TV or family. Give each child who will be asking a question a card with a question word and symbol on it. The child who is chosen to start must ask a question about the topic using the question word on their card, for example, '*What* position do you play in football?' The next person in the group asks a question using the question word on their card, for example, '*Who* is your favourite football player?', and so on. The person in the hot seat answers the questions until everyone in the group has asked one. Continue with a new person chosen to be in the hot seat.
Making it easier	Start with only one type of question. 'Who', 'what' and 'where' questions are usually the easiest ones to start with. Move up once the children are able to ask and answer that type of question.

Barrier Game with Plurals

Expected Time
Mid-length

Challenge level
Intermediate

Resources needed
- ❖ Free standing barriers. Ring binders or large books stood up on their bottom edge work well.
- ❖ Sets of small, matching objects or pictures, such as animals, furniture, food, clothes. Provide enough for each child in the group. Have single items (e.g., a table) and groups of more than one of the same item (e.g., a group of tables).
- ❖ A large pile of small, coloured bricks or counters
- ❖ The Plurals Lotto Board pictures on pages 209 and 210 in the Resources section could be used.

Aim	For children to listen to and give instructions that include plurals
Method	Before the game explain to the group that the aim of this game is to use plurals, and that we use an 's' or 'z' sound at the end of a word if we are talking about more than one thing. To give an example, pick up one of the single pictures and say what it is (e.g., 'This is a table'), then pick up the plural example and say what they are (e.g., 'These are tables'). To play the game, each child is given an identical set of small single and plural pictures. Place a barrier between the children so they cannot see each other's materials. Start off by being the 'speaker', with the children as the 'listeners'. Give instructions to the children to place a counter on a single or a plural picture. For example, 'Put a red counter on the shoes', or 'Put a blue counter on the cup'. Pass the role of the 'speaker' on to a child, and remind them to use their plural 's'. Keep swapping the role of the speaker so that everyone has a turn. Once the instructions have all been given, the barrier is removed and children compare their objects and pictures to see if they match.
Making it harder	Introduce irregular plurals such as 'sheep', 'fish', 'men'.

Plurals Lotto

Expected Time
Lengthy

Challenge level
Intermediate

Resources needed
❖ A lotto board for each child with pictures of various objects in singular and multiple form, for example, a dog/some dogs, a cat/some cats. See the Plurals Lotto Boards template on page 209 and 210 in the Resources. Use the templates and cut out and mix up the pictures to create lotto boards, so that each board has a different selection and pattern of pictures.
❖ A set of lotto cards for each board, with pictures that match those on the board

Aim For children to use regular and irregular plurals in single words

Method Give each child a lotto board and place the matching picture cards for all the boards in a pile in the middle of the group. Ensure that the children's boards are all different and that the cards are mixed up in a random order. Before starting the game explain to the group that the aim is to use plurals, and that we use an 's' or 'z' sound at the end of a word if we are talking about more than one thing. To give an example, pick up one of the single pictures and say what it is (e.g., 'This is a cat'), then pick up the plural example and say what they are (e.g., 'These are cats'). Start the game with one child picking up a picture card from the pile. They must tell the group what it is, using correct plural form, for example, 'keys'. If they have that matching picture on their lotto board they put it on top. If they do not, they have to put it on the board of the person who does have that picture. Go around the group with each child having a turn at picking up a card and saying the word. A child might say the singular form of the word when they have picked up a plural picture; for example they may say 'table' when they have picked up 'tables'. In this instance point to a picture of the singular form on someone's lotto board and tell them, 'This is table.' Ask the child, 'Do you have table or tables?' and encourage them to answer using the plural form. The first person who fills up their own board first must call out 'lotto!' and they are the winner.

Whose Is It?

Expected Time
Quick

Challenge level
Intermediate

Resources needed
❖ A picture of a boy and a girl, or a man and a woman. Puppets or dolls could also be used.
❖ Pictures such as clothing, toys, food and accessories that can be people's possessions. Toy objects could also be used.

Aim	To use possessive pronouns in a short phrase
Method	Tell the children that you are going to be talking about how, when people own things, we say the possessions are 'his' and 'hers'. Place a picture of a boy and a picture of a girl in the centre of the group. Place a pile of the pictures of their possessions near you. Check the children's understanding of the pronouns by first asking each child to point to which person would be linked to the word 'his' and which would be linked to 'hers'. Ask the first child to choose an object or picture from the pile of possessions. They can choose who to give it to, either the boy or the girl. When they have placed the item with the person, ask them who has that item. In other words, if a bag was given to the girl, ask, 'Whose bag is it?' Encourage the children to answer with the appropriate possessive pronoun, for example, 'It's his', or 'It's hers'. If the child uses the incorrect pronoun, model a choice of the answers, saying, 'Is it "his" or "hers"?'
Making it easier	Write down the words 'his' and 'hers' and place them next to the boy and girl respectively. Point to the words as needed.
Making it harder	Reduce the amount of modelling at the start of the activity.

Telling News

Expected Time Mid-length	**Resources needed** None

Challenge level Intermediate

Aim	To be able to describe personal experiences using regular or irregular past tense markers on verbs
Method	Start by telling the group some interesting news about something that has happened in the past. Tell the children to listen out for words that told them that this had already happened. These may be time words (e.g., 'yesterday', 'last' night) or past tense verbs (e.g., 'played', 'went'). Go around the group and ask each child to have a turn at telling their own news. Prompt children to use past tense verb endings. If a child leaves off a past tense ending, or uses the wrong one, repeat back what they have said and ask the child which one sounds right. For example, 'Which one sounds right? "I swimmed at the pool", or "I swam at the pool?"' Or, 'You said "I cook a cake". Should it be "I cook a cake", or "I cooked a cake?"'
Making it easier	Use visual prompts such photographs or objects related to the event, so that the children do not have to think of or remember their own news on the spot.

Support the children to tell a complete story and to use connective words by having a visual prompt on the table with these headings in boxes: |

Who	When	What	Where
and then	and then	and then	in the end

Describe the Photo

Expected Time
Mid-length

Challenge level
Intermediate

Resources needed
Photographs of the children doing activities, such as a school trip or a special event.

Aim	To describe pictures of real events using regular or irregular past tense markers on verbs
Method	Gather the photographs for this activity first. Many teachers now use photographs to record children's work and memorable events at school, so it may be possible to ask them to help. To start the activity, choose a photo that shows an event which happened in the past, for example, last week, yesterday. Describe what happened in the picture to give the children a model of the sentence that they need to use. Take another picture and call on a child to describe it by asking, 'What happened?' Encourage the child to use a sentence and verb with a past tense ending. If a child leaves off a past tense ending, or uses the wrong one, repeat back what they have said and ask the child which one sounds right. For example, 'Which one sounds right? "Sheree *goed* down the slide", or "Sheree *went* down the slide?"' Continue with more pictures and go around the group so that each child has a turn at describing one.
Making it harder	Ask children to remember a recent event and describe it, but without a photograph to refer to.

Tell the Story Sequence

Expected Time
Mid-length

Resources needed
Sets of two or three picture sequences

Challenge level
Intermediate

Aim	To re-tell a short story using pictures in a sequence
Method	Place each picture in the story out in front of the children and show them how a story goes from left to right. Ask the children to listen to you telling the story first, and then it will be their turn. Describe the sequence of pictures, modelling use of ordinal and connective words such as 'first' and 'then', as well as past tense endings. Emphasise these words. Choose children to have a turn at re-telling the story sequence, and encourage them to do this in their own words. If a child leaves off a past tense ending, or uses the wrong one, repeat back what they have said and ask the child which one sounds right. For example: 'Which one sounds right? "The girl *swimmed* in the pool", or "The girl *swam* in the pool"?'; or, 'You said, "then he cook a cake". Should it be "he *cook* a cake", or "he *cooked* a cake"?'
Making it harder	Focus on a specific structure that you want the children to use in their re-tells, for example, verbs with regular past tense endings, connective words such as 'and then'.
	You could also use longer sequences with more pictures to make this more challenging.

Now and Then

Expected Time
Mid-length

Resources needed
Picture sequences in two parts

Challenge level
Advanced

Aim	To describe a two part story in a sequence To use past tense verbs
Method	Place the first picture from one of the picture sequences out in front of the children. Describe what is happening using the word 'now' (e.g., 'The boy is playing football now'). Add the second picture and describe what happens in that picture (e.g., 'but then he kicked the ball through a window and lost his ball'). Ask the children to listen out and identify the past tense ending on your words. It is then the children's turn to describe a different story sequence, using past tense verb endings. For example, 'The boy was at home, then he walked to school.' If a child leaves off a past tense ending, or uses the wrong one, repeat back what they have said and ask the child which one sounds right. For example: 'Which one sounds right? "The girl *swimmed* in the pool", or "The girl *swam* in the pool"?'; or, 'You said "then he *cook* a cake". Should it be he *cook* a cake or he *cooked* a cake?'
Making it harder	Focus on a specific structure that you want the children to use in their re-tells, for example, verbs with regular past tense endings, connective words such as 'and then'. You could also use longer sequences with more pictures to make this more challenging.

Treasure Map

Expected Time
Mid-length

Challenge level
Advanced

Resources needed
❖ A very simple drawn map of an island with six or more landmarks and a ship off the coast. Copy and laminate a map for each child.
❖ Dry-wipe marker pens for each child

Aim	To follow and to give a series of instructions involving directional language
Method	Give everyone in the group a map. Choose a child to be the pirate who is going to bury their treasure. They must hide their map from view and mark an X on it to indicate where the treasure is buried. Then the pirate must describe to the rest of the group how to get from the ship to the treasure. Prompt the children to use specific directional language, for example, 'cross over the river, go through the trees, and turn left'. The other children need to listen carefully and draw the route on their maps. Encourage children to say when they are confused, and to ask for a repetition. When the pirate has given all the instructions, and the treasure has been 'found', the children can call out 'Shiver me timbers!' Ask the group to compare their maps and check if they drew the same route.
Making it easier	Before starting, recap the group's understanding of directional language such as left, right, next to, through. Use a prompt sheet with these written words or with symbols.

Roll the Dice

Expected Time
Mid-length

Challenge level
Advanced

Resources needed
❖ Dice
❖ Paper or whiteboard
❖ Pen

Aim   To use longer and more complex sentences and check that they make sense

Method   Decide on an interesting word and write it on the paper for the group to see. The word could be linked to a topic or theme the children have been learning about in class. Choose a child to roll the dice. Whatever number comes up will determine how many words that child needs to add to the topic word in order to make a sentence. For example, if the topic word was 'giraffe' and they roll a four, they need to make up a sentence with 'giraffe' plus four more words. For example, 'A giraffe is very tall.' Repeat the child's sentence back to them or write it down so they can hear or read it back. The child must decide if their sentence makes sense. Continue around the group with each child rolling the dice and making a sentence. Change the topic word after everyone has rolled once.

Expressive Language in the Classroom

There are many spoken language opportunities in the classroom. It is important that children with expressive language difficulties are given the chance to listen to and practise using their spoken language in the context of their peers. Here are some ways to support children's expressive communication within the classroom environment.

1 Ensure that the child has many opportunities to hear language that is just a step above what they are using themselves. If it is too complex they will not easily understand it, but if it is at the right level they will be able to use it as a model for how they can communicate.

2 In whole class discussions give the child extra time to respond. This will allow them more time to plan and order what they want to say. Give advance notice that you are going to ask a particular child to say something, for example, 'In a few moments I want you to tell me an answer', or, 'James is talking now, I'll be asking you next.'

3 Use other children as good models of language. During whole class discussions, ask other children first before asking the child with expressive language difficulties for their answer. This way they get to hear a model of what they are supposed to say before it is their turn.

4 Offer many opportunities for children to contribute verbally. Some children are reluctant talkers or just beginning to use their spoken language in the classroom. For these children offer a choice between two alternative answers (e.g., 'Was it the big scary lion or the angry elephant?'). The child then has a language model to and a reason to communicate an answer.

5 When children use minimal language, expand on what they have said by adding on one more word. For example:

Child says: 'Drink.'
Adult says: 'More drink?'

or

Child says: 'My favourite lesson is swimming.'
Adult says: 'My favourite lesson is swimming, because …?'

Page 1 of 2

Expressive Language in the Classroom

6 When a child makes a comment or gives a short answer, show interest in what they have said and prompt them gently to expand. For example, 'That sounds interesting, can you tell me more?'

7 If a child makes a grammatical error, repeat what they have said with a model of the correct grammatical structure. For example:

Child says: 'I *goed* shopping.'
Adult says: 'Oh, you *went* shopping?'

Do not expect the child to then repeat these grammatical corrections every time, but ensure that that they hear the correct model.

8 Accept different forms of communication as valid and watch out for how children communicate without using speech. Accept and praise attempts at communication, including gesture, pointing, eye pointing, use of pictures/symbols, Makaton, PECS, and augmentative and alternative communication aids.

Vocabulary

Children need to learn and use a wide range of vocabulary and concepts as they go through school. Difficulties with understanding and using vocabulary affects children's learning of new concepts, and their ability to show what they understand and get their message across.

These activities will give children opportunities to learn simple vocabulary to use in their everyday lives. There is also a focus on giving children more exposure to vocabulary related to the curriculum, so that they can become more confident with the words used in the classroom.

It is important to spend some time selecting the words that are going to be targeted in the groups. Try to find pictures of the target words so that they can be used in fun activities. Look in sets of commercial vocabulary cards, or make up your own resources by looking in magazines or on the computer.

Discuss with a teacher what the next topic in class will be. This will help with selecting the words that the children really need to know to participate in those lessons.

Indicators of Difficulties with Vocabulary

Children who have difficulties with vocabulary, concepts and word finding may display these features:

❖ difficulty remembering new vocabulary that has been taught;

❖ difficulty recalling words or selecting the exact word, for example, the child says 'clock' when 'watch' would be more accurate;

❖ limited range of vocabulary, for example, uses just nouns and verbs but not many adjectives;

❖ overuse of non-specific language, e.g., saying 'it' or 'thingy';

❖ may talk at length but the information conveyed is very limited; and

❖ searching for words or saying, 'What's it called?' in the middle of sentences.

Vocabulary Targets

1 To use general vocabulary to name and describe familiar objects or pictures

2 To sort objects or pictures into categories

3 To match objects or pictures that are semantically related (e.g. leaf and tree)

4 To name words within a category

5 To use classroom topic vocabulary to name and describe objects or pictures

6 To use adjectives to describe objects or pictures

7 To use words that are linked to concepts such as size, shape, texture or emotions

8 To use more specific words from a wider range of topics, including curriculum topics

9 To identify specific words that are semantically related

10 To use descriptive vocabulary to describe similarities and differences between objects or pictures

Special Note: Using Understanding & Auditory Memory Activities as Vocabulary Activities

The 'Barrier Game' activities described in the 'Understanding & Auditory Memory' section of this book can also be used as vocabulary activities. Just ask the child to take on the role of the speaker rather than listener. Focus using specific types of words, for example, colour and size concept words. When doing this, ensure that the child has had opportunities to hear examples of the words they need to use. They may need to hear the adult use examples of the target vocabulary several times before they can use it independently.

Descriptions of how to play 'Barrier games' can be found on pages 74 and 76 in the 'Understanding & Auditory Memory' section:

❖ Barrier Game (see p. 74)

❖ Barrier Game Sequence (see p. 76)

Vocabulary

What's in the Box?

Expected Time Quick	**Resources needed**
Challenge level Beginner	❖ A box ❖ A range of simple objects that the children are familiar with. Where possible use objects that link to the class topic. Instead of a box you could use an opaque bag, and the game can be called 'What's in the bag?'

Aim	To name familiar objects or words related to the curriculum
Method	Put a box in the centre of the group and then place a pile of objects next to it. Pick up each item and name it as it is put into the box. Ask the group, 'What's in the box?' For a group of younger children this can be turned into a song to the tune of 'The farmer's in the den' (the lyrics could be: What's in the box? What's in the box? Tell me, tell me, what's in the box?) Each child has a turn at picking out an object and naming it. If a child does not know a word, ask them to talk about what they do know about it. Use prompt questions, such as 'What is it used for?', or 'What sound does it start with?' (See the questions and symbols given in Resources, Describing Prompt Sheet.) Continue around the group until everyone has had a turn or all of the objects have been named.
Helpful hint	Regularly update and replace the objects in the box, to ensure children are learning new words.
Making it harder	Use less familiar vocabulary. Do not name the items at the start of the activity.

Posting Pictures

Expected Time Quick	**Resources needed** ❖ A posting box, which can be made by covering a shoebox in wrapping paper and cutting a posting hole in it. ❖ Small pictures of target words
Challenge level Beginner	

Aim	To name familiar pictures or words related to the curriculum
Method	Place a pile of the target pictures in the middle of the group. Choose a child to post the first picture. They must pick up a picture and try to name it. If a child does not know the word, ask them to talk about what they do know about it. Use prompt questions, such as 'What is it used for?', or 'What sound does it start with?' (See the questions and symbols given in Resources, Describing Prompt Sheet.) Continue around the group until everyone has had a turn at posting a picture or until all of the pictures have been used.
Helpful hint	Some children can be in a rush to post their picture. Ensure that they have looked at it carefully and named it before it goes into the box.
Making it harder	Use less familiar vocabulary.

Fishing for Pictures

Expected Time
Mid-length

Challenge level
Beginner

Resources needed
❖ Small pictures of target words
❖ Toy fishing rod with magnet
❖ Fish-shaped cards
❖ Paper clips
See instructions on how to prepare the fishing resources in Resources, Fishing Game Template, p. 207.)

Vocabulary

Aim	To name familiar pictures or words related to the curriculum
Method	Attach each small picture onto a fish with a paperclip. Place the fish down on the table or the floor, so that the picture is face down. Choose a child to start fishing. They need to pick up a fish with the magnet on the fishing rod. When they catch a fish they have to name the picture. If a child does not know the word, ask them to talk about what they do know about it. Use prompt questions, such as 'What is it used for?', or 'What sound does it start with?' (See the questions and symbols given in Resources, Describing Prompt Sheet.) Continue around the group until everyone has had a turn at fishing or until all of the fish have been caught.
Making it harder	Use less familiar vocabulary.

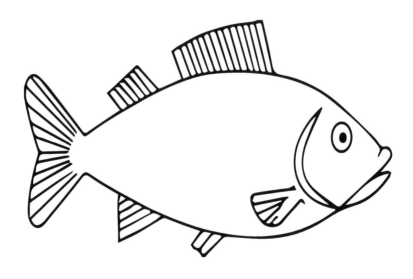

Hula Hoop Sorting

Expected Time
Mid-length

Challenge level
Beginner

Resources needed
- ❖ Objects or toys belonging to the same basic categories, for example, food, transport, clothes, animals, furniture. Start with just two different categories. Picture cards could also be used.
- ❖ Two large hula hoops, or two boxes

Aim	To sort items into categories
Method	Place two hoops on the floor in the middle of the group. Place a pile of mixed-up objects from two categories on the floor or table. Start by giving the children an example of what you want them to do. Place an object from one category into a hoop and an object from the other category into the other hoop. Then it is the first child's turn to pick up an object. They must name it, and decide which hoop it belongs in. Continue around the group with each child adding another object to the hoops. Once all the objects have been sorted, ask the children what the name of each category is. This is harder, so prompt the children by asking them to look more closely at the objects. Ask, 'What do you do with it?', and 'What other things is it like?', or 'Where do you find it?'
Making it easier	Choose two categories that are quite different, for example, animals and food. This will make sorting easier.
Making it harder	Select closely related categories, for example, fruit and vegetables. For more of a challenge, have three categories and three hoops.

Vocabulary

Things that Go Together

<table>
<tr><td>

Expected Time
Mid-length

Challenge level
Beginner
</td><td>

Resources needed
Pairs of items that go together, for example, pencil and eraser, leaf and tree. There are commercially available sets of these picture cards, or they can easily be made.
</td></tr>
</table>

Aim	To identify items which are semantically linked
Method	Place up to eight pictures on the table or floor in front of the group. Make sure they are mixed up. Ask the children to take turns to find two pictures that go together. Each child then picks up their pair, and says the names of the items. They can then keep their pair. Continue going around the group until all of the pictures have been used up.
Making it harder	When a child picks up a pair, ask them to explain why or how the items go together.

Find Your Partner

Resources needed
Pairs of items that go together, for example, pencil and eraser, leaf and tree. There are commercially available sets of these picture cards, or they can easily be made. At least one set for each player is needed.

Aim	To identify items which are semantically associated
Method	Hand out pictures randomly to each child. Ask the children to look at their picture carefully. Explain to the group that on the count of three everyone has to stand up and find their partner. This will be the person who has the picture that goes with theirs. Once everyone has found their partner, ask the group to sit down again. Ask each pair to hold up their picture and one child has to explain why those pictures go together.

Vocabulary

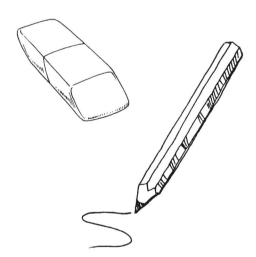

What Am I?

<table>
<tr><td>Expected Time
Mid-length</td><td>Resources needed
Pictures of common objects</td></tr>
</table>

Challenge level
Intermediate

Aim	For children to identify a word from descriptive clues
Method	Have a pile of pictures and select one, but do not show it to the group. Give the children three clues that describe the item, for example, 'I am small, I have a tail, I like cheese. What am I?' (mouse). Explain that they have to wait until they have heard all three clues before guessing what it is. When all children have guessed, show the picture to the group.
Helpful hint	Ask children to put their hand up when they think they know what the picture is, rather than calling out. Some children may be quicker than others and this will allow everyone to have time to think.
Making it easier	Add a clue by giving the first sound in the word, for example, 'I am small, I have a tail, I like cheese. My name starts with "m". What am I?' (mouse).
Making it harder	Select pictures from a specific topic, or select less familiar items. Using pictures of actions (verbs) instead of nouns will also be more challenging.

The Love Glove

Aim	For children to name things that they like within a category
Method	Show the children a glove and put it on. Explain that it is a 'love glove' and that it helps you to think of things that you love. Start by giving the group an example, such as 'I love my pet dog.' Pass the glove around so that each child puts it on in turn and says what they love. The first time around let the children say the name of something they love from any category, for example, TV shows, family, football teams, food. After everyone has had a turn, choose a specific category for the group. The children then have to pass around the glove and say their favourite thing in that category, for example their favourite TV show or favourite food.

Vocabulary

Pass the Category

Expected Time	**Resources needed**
Quick	❖ Opaque bag
	❖ Interesting objects with different features and from different categories. Picture cards could also be used.

Challenge level
Intermediate

Aim	To name items within a category
Method	Place all the objects into the opaque bag. Ask the first child to take an object out of the bag. They have to say what it is and what category it belongs to. For example, 'A fork. It belongs to the category kitchen things.' Pass that object around the group, and when each child receives the object they have to say another word that belongs to that category, for example, a plate, a fridge. The next child then chooses an object out of the bag and the game continues in the same way.
Making it harder	Instead of asking the group to name the category, make the focus on using adjectives. When the first child chooses their object, they have to describe it using an adjective such as 'shiny'. The other children then need to name items that could also be described in that manner.

Beanbag Categories

Aim	To name items in a category rapidly
Method	Take a beanbag and explain to the group that when someone catches it they have to say a word. Introduce a category, for example, fruits. Start by saying a word from that category, for example, banana. Then pass the beanbag on to someone else in the group. They have to say another word from that category before passing it on to the next person. Continue going around the group rapidly. If someone repeats a word that has already been said they have to take the beanbag back and try to think of a new one. Continue until the children have run out of words to add.
Making it harder	Introduce a different coloured beanbag, and choose a new category for it. Pass the new bag around whilst the original bag is still going. The children need to look carefully at where the beanbags are, listen out for the words that have already been said, and remember which bag is for which category. It can be a challenge!

Vocabulary

Magic Glasses or Goggles

Expected Time
Mid-length

Challenge level
Intermediate

Resources needed
- A pair of toy glasses or
- A pair of goggles

Aim	For children to be able to identify a place after hearing a description of it
Method	Children take it in turns to put on a pair of 'magic' goggles or glasses. Explain to the children that when they put on the magic goggles or glasses they will be able to see through to a particular place by using their imagination. The child whose turn it is decides what the place is, but does not tell the others. Then they must describe to the other children some things they can see in that place. The other children take turns at guessing what the place is, for example, 'I can see a cash register, some sweets, a carrot, and a trolley [the supermarket].' The glasses or goggles are passed on to the next child who has a turn at imagining.
Making it easier	Decide on a location for the children to imagine they are in, for example, the seaside, the classroom, the fruit market. Pass the goggles around the group and ask each child to think of something they can see in that place.

Build the Category

Expected Time
Quick

Resources needed
None

Challenge level
Intermediate

Aim	To name items in a category, without knowing the category name
Method	Start by telling the group that you are thinking of a category. Choose the category (e.g., kitchen things), but do not tell the group what it is. Instead say a word from that category (e.g., kettle). The next child must try to add an item from the same category (e.g., cooker). This continues around the group. Once everyone has had a turn at naming an item, ask the group if they know which category it is in.
Helpful hint	When it comes to the group having to say the name of the category, encourage them to put their hands up, rather than calling out. This gives all of the children a chance to think and find the specific word.
Making it easier	If the children are struggling to think of something else in that category, give a few more examples of words before you ask them to add one themselves.

Vocabulary

I Give You this Gift

Vocabulary

Expected Time Quick	**Resources needed** ❖ An opaque bag or a box ❖ A selection of toys or objects that have a different appearance, texture, function and size
Challenge level Intermediate	

Aim

To use simple adjectives in sentences

Method

Tell the group that they will be choosing a 'gift' from the bag to give to someone else in the group. They will need to describe their gift using an adjective (a 'describing' word). Ask the group to call out words that could be used to describe objects, and write these on paper or a whiteboard. Prompt the children to think about colour, size, texture or specific attributes. Start the activity by choosing the first 'gift' and giving it to one of the children. Use the sentence, 'I give you this gift because …', and add in a suitable adjective. For example, 'I give you this gift because it is shiny.' This child then chooses a gift for the next child. Continue around the group so that everyone has a turn. Prompt the children to use some of the words that they came up with at the beginning of the game.

Making it harder

Ask the child who receives the gift to think of something else that could be described in the same way. For example, if the gift was a shiny coin, then they could say 'a shiny necklace'.

Guess the Emotion

Expected Time Mid-length	**Resources needed** Pictures or photos of people with facial expressions or body language clearly showing their emotions. These are commercially available or they can easily be drawn or made. Choose a set of emotion words such as happy, sad, angry, scared, disappointed and embarrassed.
Challenge level Intermediate	

Aim	To name emotion words acted out by another person
Method	Choose one child to be the first actor. Show them an emotion picture and tell them not to show it to the rest of the group. This child then needs to act out that emotion to the group, using their body language and facial expression. The other children in the group must guess what the emotion is, using the specific word. The actor reveals their card and the group check if they were right. Continue going around the group until everyone has had a turn at acting.
Helpful hint	When the group are guessing the emotion, encourage them to put their hands up, rather than calling out. This gives all of the children a chance to think of the specific word.
Making it harder	After each turn, show the card to the group and discuss why this child might be feeling this way.

Vocabulary

On Topic

<table>
<tr><td>

Expected Time
Mid-length

Challenge level
Intermediate

</td></tr>
</table>

Resources needed
- ❖ Symbols or written words to indicate the name of the topic (optional)
- ❖ Egg timer

Aim	To name items in a category rapidly
Method	Separate the group into two smaller groups. Choose one child to be the scribe (ensure that they feel confident to write). Name a topic, for example, things with wheels. Turn over an egg timer and tell the group that they have two minutes to think of and write down as many words in that category as possible. At the end of the two minutes ask the smaller groups to share their answers with the whole group.
Making it easier	Start off with simple categories such as animals. Allow more than two minutes. An adult is the scribe rather than a child.
Making it harder	Choose more specific categories, for example, animals with four legs.

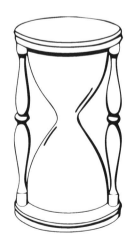

Nouns and Adjectives

Expected Time
Mid-length

Resources needed
A small beanbag

Challenge level
Advanced

Aim	To name words in a specific category and use adjectives to describe them
Method	Split the group into two smaller groups. Tell one group that they are the nouns and the other group that they are the adjectives. Choose a topic (e.g. animals), and hand a beanbag to a child in the noun group. They have to say a noun from that category, for example, tiger. When they have said their word, they have to pass the beanbag to the adjective group. The children in the adjective group have to say a word that describes that noun, for example, fierce. The beanbag is then passed back to the noun group for them to add another word. This continues back and forth.

Vocabulary

Twenty Questions

Expected Time Lengthy	**Resources needed** A selection of pictures of interesting and familiar items
Challenge level Advanced	

Aim	To deduce what a word is by asking a series of questions
Method	Choose a child to start, and they can take a picture of an object from a pile. Tell them to look at the picture but not to show it to the rest of the group. The other children have to try to find out what the picture is by asking questions. The questions must be ones that can only be answered with a 'yes' or a 'no'. Encourage pupils to ask specific questions. For example: 'Is it an animal?', 'Can you eat it?', 'Does it have legs?', and 'Is it alive?' It is important that the group listen to the questions and answers have been given before, because this will help them to guess the word. Go around the group twice, so that everyone has asked at least two questions each before anyone takes a guess. If someone takes a guess and it is not correct, continue going around the group and asking questions.
Making it easier	Write down the questions on a board as they are asked, so the children can remember what has been said. After every few questions summarise what the group knows about the item so far.

Word Associations

Aim	For children to think of words that have a connection to each other
Method	Ask a child to think of any word and say it aloud to the group. The adult says a different word that is related somehow to it. The next child has to add on another word that is related to that one. It does not need to be related to the first word. For example, Egypt – mummy – daddy. Ask the group to keep adding on words that are related to the last one. If children cannot follow the connection between the words, pause and explain how they are linked. Keep going around until everyone has run out of words to add.
Making it easier	Write down the words as you go along.

Vocabulary

Continuum

Expected Time
Mid-length

Challenge level
Advanced

Resources needed
❖ Flip chart or whiteboard
❖ Pen

Aim   To identify words that link to an adjective along a continuum

Method   Choose two adjective words that are at different points on a continuum, for example, hot and cold, big and little, stormy and calm. Write the words at each end of a long line to indicate the continuum. Ask the group to think of words that can be described by these words. For example, for hot and cold suitable words could be coffee, fire, water, ice and snow.

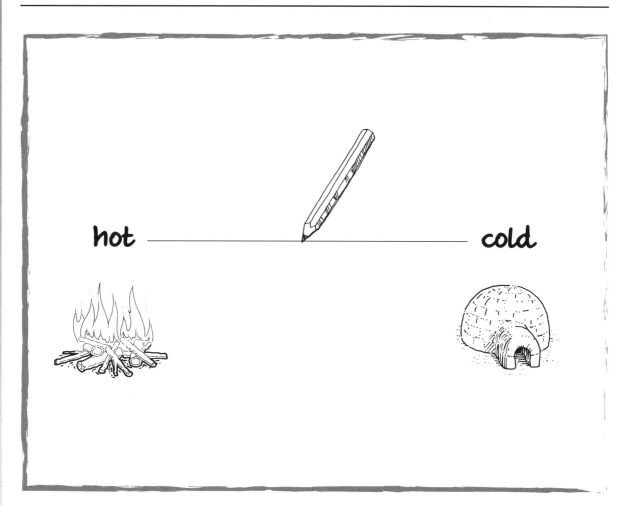

hot ———————— cold

Similarities and Differences

Expected Time	Resources needed
Mid-length	❖ Opaque bag
	❖ A mixture of interesting objects with different functions, sizes, shapes and appearances

Challenge level
Advanced

Aim	To identify features that are similar and different in objects
Method	Place a selection of interesting objects in an opaque bag. Start by giving the children an example of what you want them to do. Pull out two objects and name them. Then explain that they need to say one thing that is the same about these things, for example, 'They are both red.' Then they need to say one thing that is different, for example, 'This one is for writing (a red pen), and 'This one is for eating' (a red apple). Go around the group with each child pulling out two random objects. If a child has difficulties identifying the most salient features, prompt them using a Describing Prompt Sheet such as the one in the Resources (p. 216). Call on other children in the group to add features if one child is particularly struggling with ideas.
Making it harder	Select items that are more closely related.

Comparison Brainstorm

Expected Time
Lengthy

Challenge level
Advanced

Resources needed
❖ Flip chart paper or a whiteboard
❖ Pen

Aim	To compare features of two semantically related items
Method	Choose a particular word (e.g., bicycle), and write it on a flipchart. Ask the group to do a brainstorm where they say everything they know about this item. Write down the children's responses. Then do the same for a word from the same category (e.g., car). Prompt children to say things that are the most important characteristics of that item. Ask the group to look at what they said and identify what is the same about the words and what is different.
Making it easier	Rather than comparing similarities and differences for two items, just brainstorm features of one word.

Vocabulary in the Classroom

The classroom is the ideal environment to develop children's vocabulary. It is where they learn a great deal of their new words, and it is important to dedicate time to introducing and teaching those words in the context of a lesson with practical activities. Here are some ways to support those children who need help with learning and using vocabulary.

1   When introducing a new topic, use a mind map. A mind map has a topic in the centre of the page and lines coming off it to show children how the new words they are learning link to it. When finishing up a unit of work on a particular topic, encourage the children to fill in a mind map together to show them all the new words they have learned. Mind maps work well with pictures as well as writing.

2   When introducing new vocabulary, talk about all aspects of the word. Discuss with the class:

   ❖ which category the word is in;

   ❖ the sound properties of that word (i.e., what letter sound it starts with, or number of syllables);

   ❖ the function (i.e., what it does or what it is used for); and

   ❖ the appearance , i.e. what the object looks like and how it could be described

3   When a child is stuck and cannot find the word they want to use, support them to retrieve the word. Rather than telling them the word, ask questions to help them locate the word in their vocabulary. For example, if they are trying to find the word 'fork', you could ask these questions:

   ❖ What do you do with it?

   ❖ Where do you find it?

   ❖ What is special about it?

   ❖ What sound does it start with?

Page 1 of 2

Vocabulary in the Classroom

4 Widen children's vocabularies through stories. Select books with interesting words that are at the right level for their language. If reading is difficult they can be read to by an adult. As new, long or interesting words come up in the story point these out. Write the words down and go back and discuss what these words mean once you have finished reading.

5 Give children lots of exposure to new words by showing them and saying them as much as possible. Add new topic words or tricky words from books to a word wall in the classroom, or simply write them on the board during a lesson. Doing this is a good reminder for the adults and children to talk about those words at different times in the day, in different contexts.

6 Teach and reinforce new vocabulary using a 'new words book'. Give a child an exercise book for them to write down words and pictures that are new in each lesson, or those that they found tricky while reading a book. When they have finished their work and have spare time, they can look up the meaning in a dictionary or on the computer.

Problem Solving & Verbal Reasoning

Verbal reasoning is a skill that is essential for understanding social situations and learning in the classroom. It involves understanding and answering 'how' and 'why' something has happened and is fundamental for solving social problems. In order to think through and solve problems, children need to use their internal language, or 'self-talk', so when a child has difficulties with understanding and using spoken language they will usually have difficulties with verbal reasoning.

Many problem-solving skills are learnt through experience of normal social interaction. Children with communication difficulties can benefit from talking through problems in detail as they arise, but also by practising problem solving in specific activities such as the ones presented in this section.

Indicators of Difficulty with Problem Solving & Verbal Reasoning

Children who have difficulties with problem solving and verbal reasoning may display these features:

❖ following simple instructions, but difficulties in understanding abstract language and ideas;

❖ difficulties making predictions about what might happen next in social situations or in a story;

❖ may have difficulties understanding other people's points of view or feelings;

❖ difficulties understanding the implications of an event, or seeing the relationship with a cause and an effect; and

❖ taking things literally, not always picking up on the subtleties of language.

Problem Solving & Verbal Reasoning Targets

1 To give an explanation of how something works

2 To make predictions about what might happen next, linked to a story or a picture

3 To explain possible reasons or causes of problems and situations

4 To explain possible solutions to a problem

5 To answer 'how do you know' questions to give reasons for answers

101 Uses

Resources needed
A new, interesting object each session. Good ones to use are a roll of sellotape, a spanner, a scarf, a paper clip, a jar, mirror, a toilet roll, or a ruler.

Aim	To think creatively about how to use an object
Method	Show the children the chosen object. The children need to think of as many uses for this thing as possible. For example, a roll of sellotape could be used to repair broken glasses, to stick a picture to the wall, or it could be worn on the wrist as a bangle. Accept silly ideas as long as the child can explain how to use it. Ensure that everyone has a chance to suggest an idea by going around the group. Count up the number of ideas the group thought of. Play the game each week and see if they can beat their last score.

Problem Solving & Verbal Reasoning

Alien at School

Expected Time
Mid-length

Resources needed
Alien toy or a picture of an alien

Challenge level
Intermediate

Aim	To explain school routines
Method	Show the alien to the group and tell them that he has just landed from outer space and is coming to their school. Explain that he does not know anything about what to do at school, so the group needs to help him by describing parts of the day. Have a list of familiar school routines and ask each child in turn to explain what to do, for example, 'What happens at lunchtime?', 'What do you do when the bell rings?', and 'How do you find your classroom?' As the children give their explanations, remind them that the alien does not know what some of the words mean (e.g., assembly), so they will need to be very specific in their explanations. Continue around the group with each child describing a different school routine.
Making it harder	Ask the children to describe multiple-step sequences, such as the route to school, or 'What do you do if you have a school dinner?'

What Next?

Expected Time
Mid-length

Challenge level
Intermediate

Resources needed
Sets of picture sequences, with 3 or more cards. There are many commercially available sets of these pictures. They could also be made by copying pages of a picture book and making them into cards.

Aim	To make predictions about what would happen next in a story.
Method	Order the first two sequencing cards and place them in the middle of the group. Describe the story depicted in the pictures or ask one child to describe what is happening. Each child is then asked to predict what they think might happen in the next picture. Once everyone has had a turn reveal the next card to see if anyone was right. Keep doing this until all the pictures have been revealed.
Helpful hint	Start with three-picture sequences and build up to longer sets.

What's Going On?

Expected Time
Mid-length

Challenge level
Intermediate

Resources needed
Social scene pictures. There are commercially available packs of these. Pictures from the newspaper or illustrated children's books could also be used.

Aim	To be able to answer questions about a social scenario
Method	Show the group a picture of a social scene. Encourage children to look carefully and describe it. Ask concrete questions about things that are obvious from the picture, for example, 'Who is in the picture?', and 'What is going on?' Then move on to questions that are not immediately obvious about the scene. These questions should require the children to use inference or problem solving, for example, 'Why is he doing that?', 'What might happen next?', and 'What would you do?'
Making it easier/ harder	This activity can be varied by asking more abstract questions or using more ambiguous picture scenes.

The Emotions Game

Expected Time Quick	**Resources needed** Pictures or photos of people with facial expressions or body language clearly showing their emotions. These are commercially available or they can easily be drawn or made. Choose a set of emotion words such as happy, sad, angry, scared, disappointed, and embarrassed.
Challenge level Intermediate	

Aim To be able to identify causes of different emotions

Method Place the emotions cards face down in the middle of the group. The first child has to pick up a card and name the emotion that the person is displaying, for example, angry, happy, excited. Ask them, 'Why might the person feel like that?' Go around the group and ask each child to say a time that they felt the same way. Continue around the group, with the next child choosing a card showing a different emotion.

Making it easier Before looking at the pictures, brainstorm a range of emotion words. Write these up on a chart for the children to refer to.

Why/Because

Expected Time
Mid-length

Challenge level
Advanced

Resources needed
- ❖ Cards with 'why' questions about familiar situations for school children (see Resources, Why/Because Cards, p. 212, for examples, or make up some of your own).
- ❖ Box to put the cards in. A bag could also be used.

Aim	To answer 'why' questions with an explanation, reason or opinion
Method	Cut up the question cards and put them in the box. The first child selects a card from the box, and they read that question to the person on their left. That child must then answer the question. Prompt the child to use an answer that starts with 'because'. If children are struggling to explain an answer, give some possible reasons and ask them to choose which one makes sense. Continue around until everyone has asked and answered a question.
Helpful hint	Regularly change the questions on the cards to add variety.
Making it harder	For each question ask everyone in the group to suggest a reason. Write them all down and discuss which one is the best answer. Sometimes there will be more than one good reason.

Simple Solutions

Expected Time
Mid-length

Challenge level
Advanced

Resources needed
❖ Cards with 'What would you do if …?' questions about familiar problems for school children (see Resources, Simple Solution Cards, p. 213, for some examples, or make up your own).
❖ Box to put the cards in. A bag could also be used.

Aim	To be able to provide solutions to familiar social problems
Method	Cut up the question cards and put them in the box. The first child selects a card from the box, and they read that question to the person on their left. That child must then think of how they would respond in that situation. Go around the group and ask everyone to say what they would do to solve that problem. Accept answers that may not be the most appropriate, but ask the child to explain why they would choose the solution they offered. Once everyone has made a suggestion, the group discusses and decides which answer is the best. If children are struggling to think of a suitable solution, give some suggestions and ask them to choose which one would work. Continue around the group so that everyone gets to choose a new problem card from the box.
Making it harder	Get children to think of real problems that have happened to them. Write these down on cards and add these to the box. Give the children homework to go and ask other children how they would respond to a situation that was discussed in the group.

How Do You Know?

Expected Time
Mid-length

Challenge level
Advanced

Resources needed
- ❖ A busy picture scene with lots of different things happening in it or
- ❖ A descriptive paragraph from a book

Aim	For children to provide reasons for their judgements
Method	Show the picture or read the text to the group. Ask children questions about the picture or text. Use a mixture of questions that are obvious (e.g., 'Who is driving the bus?'), and ones that are not immediately observable and require the use of inference or judgement (e.g., 'What time of year is it?', or 'How is she feeling?'). Follow each question up with 'How do you know?' questions. This encourages children to give reasons for their answers and explain their thinking. Examples could include:

- ❖ What season is it? How do you know?
- ❖ What time of day is it? How do you know?
- ❖ How is he feeling? How do you know?
- ❖ Where is she going? How do you know?

Handout 8
Problem Solving & Verbal Reasoning in the Classroom

The classroom is the ideal environment to develop children's thinking, but it is important to focus on getting them to verbalise their thinking. Encourage children with communication difficulties to talk through real examples of problems that happen at school. Here are some ways to create opportunities to support this skill in the classroom.

1 Some questions are more difficult and require a child to use more reasoning than others, so think carefully about the questions you ask. When asking questions in the classroom start with more concrete questions that are about what is obvious or can be seen, for example, 'Who is it?', or 'Where is it?' After the answers to these concrete questions have been established, move up to asking more abstract questions, for example, 'How do you know?', or 'What might happen next?'

2 Deliberately sabotage situations in the classroom so that children are required to problem solve. Wait for them to initiate solutions, and observe how they do this. For example, in a cutting and pasting activity, put the glue but not the scissors out.

3 When a pupil has difficulty understanding other people's points of view or feelings, take a step-by-step approach. Present several possible reactions to the same scenario, for example, 'If you do A, what will happen next? And if you do B, what will happen next? Which one do you think you should do?'

4 Use motivating and multi-sensory information, such as role play, TV clips, videos, or comics to develop the pupils' understanding of social situations and problems. Look at a scene together and discuss what the problems are and how to solve them.

5 Discuss real examples of social problems as a class. Talk about how the people involved would feel. Get the children to brainstorm a range of possible actions and then talk about the options. What do children think is the best thing to do? Why? Role play and 'hot seating' are great for this. Emphasise that it is acceptable that there is a range of different responses.

6 Use social situations that are encountered in a story or a film as content to think about with the whole class. Stop reading or watching for a moment to discuss what might happen next, or how the character is feeling. Ask the children to provide reasons for their answers.

Sequencing & Narrative

Sequencing ideas and thoughts is an important language skill, and is integral to many tasks that children are required to complete in school. Sequencing skills are involved in all of these tasks:

❖ knowing how to set out things from left to right, for example, writing on a page or reading a book;

❖ understanding how to do things in a certain order, for example, following instructions, organising equipment and in everyday tasks such as getting dressed;

❖ putting words in the right order in sentences, and putting sentences in the right order to express ideas clearly; and

❖ listening to and constructing verbal narratives.

Children see and hear narratives through stories in books, but they are not only encountered in fictional stories. Children and adults use narratives every day when talking about events that have happened, or when talking about things that will happen in the future. Being able to construct a narrative is an essential skill for successful social communication.

Indicators of Difficulty with Sequencing & Narrative Skills

Children who have difficulties with sequencing and narrative skills may display these features:

❖ difficulty retelling a familiar activity or event in the right order;

❖ difficulty with remembering common sequences, for example, days of the week;

❖ difficulty understanding time concepts, which may result in confusion about what is timetabled to happen next;

❖ difficulty following a series of sequential instructions;

❖ difficulties with sequencing often stand out in writing tasks, where there may be no clear structure to a child's written narrative.

Sequencing & Narrative Targets

1 To understand and use familiar sequences of words (e.g. days of the week)

2 To answer questions about the order of events using concepts of time (e.g. after) and number (e.g. first)

3 To describe a sequence of events using sequential connectives (e.g. then, next)

4 To accurately order and describe pictures from a story

5 To understand and use a story structure, including a 'setting', 'what happens' and 'ending'.

6 To re-tell a familiar story.

7 To tell an imaginative story using a story planner.

Group Sequence

Expected Time Quick	**Resources needed** Large paper with familiar sequences written on, such as the alphabet, days of the week, months of the year, numbers or seasons
Challenge level Beginner	

Aim	To recite familiar sequences
Method	Display the sequence that you are targeting on a large piece of paper. This will be a visual prompt for the children to refer to. Start by chanting the sequence, pointing to the words, letters or numbers as you say the sequence together. Take the written sequence away and see if the group can recall it all together without the visual prompt. Once the group are becoming familiar with the sequence, go around the group. Start by saying the first word (e.g., Monday), then each child has to say the one that comes next in the sequence (e.g., Tuesday). Continue around the group and encourage the children to listen carefully and only say the word when it is their turn.
Helpful hint	Target one sequence at a time, and repeat it several times in each group session.
Making it harder	Start midway through the sequence (e.g., at five when counting to ten) and go forward from there.

January	FEBRUARY	March
April	May	JUNE
July	August	September
October	November	December

Clothes Line

Expected Time
Mid-length

Challenge level
Beginner

Resources needed
- ❖ Clothes line: this could be made of string stretched between two walls.
- ❖ Pegs
- ❖ Words or symbols from familiar sequences written onto individual cards (one step per card). Suggested sequences are the alphabet, days of the week, months of the year, numbers, lessons on the school timetable, or the steps of a daily routine such as getting dressed.

Aim	To identify and complete missing items from a familiar sequence
Method	First set up the clothes line (some rooms in schools may already have string up to display children's work). Attach some of the items from the sequence being used to the clothes line using pegs. Peg them in the correct order, but with some gaps where a word is missing. Hand out the remaining items to children in the group. In turn, each child must put their item in the appropriate place on the line.
Making it easier	Before putting the cards on the clothes line, recite the sequence as a group.
Making it harder	Do not make the gaps obvious, so that the children have to think more carefully about which words are missing.

Lining Up

Expected Time
Quick

Resources needed
None

Challenge level
Beginner

Aim	To answer simple questions about order and sequence using a visual cue
Method	This activity helps to develop children's understanding and use of the language of order through lining up. Get the children to stand up and line up facing in one direction. Go along the line and say the names of the children and their order, modelling the sequential language, for example, 'Tariq is first, next is Rebecca and last is Mark.' Ask the children to answer direct questions about where they are in the order, for example, 'Who is first?', 'Who is last?', or 'Who is second?' Tell the group to move around and change order and repeat the game.
Helpful hint	This is a good activity to do at the end of the group when the children are lining up to go back to their classroom.

Sequencing & Narrative

Who Was First?

Expected Time
Quick

Resources needed
None

Challenge level
Beginner

Aim	To answer simple questions about order
Method	After any activity in the communication group use the opportunity to talk about the order that things happened. Ask questions that will encourage the children to use sequential language. When all of the children have had one turn, ask about the order in which they took turns, for example, 'Who went first?', 'Who was next?', 'Who was after them?', or 'Who was last?'
Making it easier	Incorporate this discussion into the middle of activities in the communication group, rather than waiting until the end.

'And Then ...'

Expected Time
Quick

Challenge level
Beginner

Resources needed
- ❖ Small toys or interesting objects
- ❖ A prompt card with 'and then' in words or symbols

Aim	To be able to understand and give sequential instructions using connectives
Method	Place the objects out in front of the group. Give instructions to the first child to do two things in a sequence of actions, for example, 'Clap your hands and then pick up the key.' Once this child has carried out their instruction, they have to give a two-part instruction to another child. They can ask them to do actions with the objects or just with their bodies. Prompt the children to use the connective phrase 'and then' by showing them the prompt card. Continue around the group until everyone has had a few turns at listening to and giving instructions.
Making it harder	Increase the number of instructions that the children have to listen to and give. Introduce new concepts, including 'before', 'after' and 'at the same time as'. Give instructions such as 'Before you clap your hands stand up', or 'Smile at the same time as you turn around.'

Sequencing & Narrative

What Did They Do?

Expected Time
Quick

Challenge level
Beginner

Resources needed
- ❖ Small, pretend play toys, such as kitchen toys, a telephone, teddies, a brush, and a towel
- ❖ A 'then' prompt card with the word or a symbol

Aim	To describe sequential events that have been observed
Method	Place some toys in the middle of the group. Ask the first child to do two actions with the objects, for example, drink from the cup, then stir the pan. Ask the next child, 'What did they do?' That child has to describe the sequence of actions they just observed. Show the prompt card to encourage them to link their words together using 'then'.

Order of the Day

Expected Time
Lengthy

Challenge level
Intermediate

Resources needed
❖ A sheet of blank paper for each child
❖ Pencils for each child

Aim   To order the events in the school day visually. To answer questions about the order of events

Method   Ask the group to call out different activities and lessons that happen in a school day, for example, assembly, maths, literacy, morning break, lunch, PE, home time. Give each child a sheet of blank paper and ask them to draw a picture for one activity. Make sure that each child is drawing a different activity. Gather all of the pictures together and ask the children to put them in the order that they happen, using sequential language. Support the children to get the right order by asking question such as, 'What did we do first today?', and 'What did we do next?' When all of the pictures are in order, go around the group and ask specific questions about the order of events. Use the concept words 'before' and 'after'. For example, 'What happened before literacy?', and 'What will you do after lunch?'

Finish the Sequence

<table>
<tr><td>

Expected Time
Mid-length

Challenge level
Intermediate

</td><td>

Resources needed
Sets of picture sequences. There are many commercially available sets of these pictures. They could also be made by taking photographs of the children doing simple sequential activities.

</td></tr>
</table>

Aim	To be able to order pictures in a sequence and describe what is happening
Method	Place two or more sequencing cards in the middle of the group in the right order, but leave the last picture off. Ask one child to describe what is happening in the first picture, and then the next child describes the picture after that. Call on the next child to predict what they think might happen next in the missing final picture. Reveal the last card to see if anyone was right.
Helpful hint	Start with three-picture sequences and build up to longer sets.
Making it easier	Place all of the pictures out and ask the children to look at them. Then take the final picture away. This means that the child has to remember and describe what they saw rather than making a prediction about the last picture.
Making it harder	After one child has made a prediction about the last picture, ask each child in the group to think of a different ending.

Sequencing Pictures

Expected Time	**Resources needed**
Mid-length	❖ Sets of three- to six-part picture sequences. There are many commercially available sets of these pictures. They could also be made by taking photographs of the children doing simple sequential activities.
Challenge level	❖ Visual prompts (written words or symbols) for the words 'first', 'next', 'then' and 'last'
Intermediate	

Aim	To order and describe picture sequences using sequential language
Method	Place a set of sequencing pictures in the middle of the group in order, from left to right. To provide a model, tell a story about these pictures and use connectives such as 'first', 'next' and 'last'. Display the visual prompts for these sequential words and point to them as you say them. Give each pupil a set of their own pictures to put into the right order. Go around the group and give each person a turn to tell their story. Prompt the children to use the words 'first', 'next' and 'last' by showing the visual reminder.
Helpful hint	Start with three-picture sequences and build up to longer sets.
Making it easier	Use longer sequences.

Sequence Shuffle

Expected Time Mid-length	**Resources needed** Sets of three- to six-part picture sequences. There are many commercially available sets of these pictures. They could also be made by taking photographs of the children doing simple sequential activities.
Challenge level Intermediate	

Aim	To work as a group to sequence a series of pictures
Method	Give each child in the group one picture from a sequence. Ask each child to hold up their picture and describe what is happening in it. Tell the children that when they hear 'go!' they must organise themselves to sit in the order of the story, so that each person's picture is in the right order. Say 'go!' Ask the group to then tell their story, with each person describing their part.
Helpful hint	For larger groups divide the group into smaller numbers; so, for a group of six, have two small groups with two sets of three picture sequences.
Making it harder	Use longer sequences.

Order the Story

Expected Time
Lengthy

Challenge level
Intermediate

Resources needed
❖ Children's storybooks
❖ Several photocopied pictures from the books, or drawings that reflect the sequence of events

Aim	To order and describe familiar stories using sequential language
Method	Read a short storybook to the group. Encourage the children to listen carefully, because they will need to tell the story themselves. Place four or more pictures from the story in the middle of the group. Pick up a random picture and call on a child to describe what is happening at that point in the story. Do the same for each picture to establish if the children understand what the pictures mean. Then ask a child to find the picture that goes first. Continue, asking each child to find the next picture in order. Order the pictures from left to right. Then go around the group to retell the story, with each child describing one picture.
Making it harder	Present the pictures without having read the story first.

Sequencing & Narrative

Imagine a Story

Expected Time
Lengthy

Challenge level
Advanced

Resources needed
Any children's story book. Find the description of the story setting, which is usually two to three sentences at the beginning of the story.

Aim	To visualise and add details to story setting
Method	Ask the children to listen carefully and make a picture in their heads as you read the story. Read the paragraph that describes the story setting to the group at least twice. Ask the children questions based specifically on the text, such as 'Who is in the story?', 'Where are they?', 'When did this happen?', and 'What is it like?' Then ask children to use the picture in their head and really imagine what the setting is like, including things that the author did not write about. Ask questions that are not specifically in the text, such as 'What is the weather like?', or 'What else can you see?', or 'What does the boy look like?' The children are then given some paper and pencils to make a drawing of the setting as they imagine it.
Making it harder	Use a story with more detailed descriptions and complex vocabulary.

Remember the Story

<table>
<tr><td>Expected Time
Lengthy</td><td>Resources needed
Short story or a paragraph from a longer story or book</td></tr>
</table>

Challenge level
Advanced

Aim	For children to retell a story they have listened to and answer questions about it
Method	Read a short story to the group and tell them to listen very carefully. After the story has been read, ask the children to take turns at re-telling parts of it. Go around the group so that everyone contributes. Ask some simple specific questions about the content of the story, for example, 'Who was in the story?', and 'Where were the people?' Read the story again if children have difficulties recalling the details.
Variation	Instead of reading a story, make this game relevant to other curriculum subjects by reading a paragraph from a classroom topic book such as a history, geography or science book.
Making it easier	Place a picture that relates to the story in the middle of the group. This will give the children a visual clue about what is happening and may help to focus their attention.

Sequencing & Narrative

Story Retell

Expected Time
Lengthy

Challenge level
Advanced

Resources needed
❖ A familiar short storybook
❖ Puppets or small-world toys (optional)

Aim	To be able to retell familiar stories
Method	Read the familiar short story to the group, pointing out relevant information in the pictures. Close the book. Go around the group and ask the children to retell the story, with a different child telling each part of the story. If a child forgets what happened next, prompt them by showing the corresponding page from the book. Once everyone has had a turn at telling part of the story, look back at the book together to check that they were right.
Making it easier	Give each child a puppet or toy character to act out their part of the story. This usually encourages children to use their spoken language to take on the voice of the character.

Story Starter

Expected Time
Lengthy

Challenge level
Advanced

Resources needed

❖ Story planner, using words or symbols to represent the essential parts of a story. For example: who, where, when, what happened, what happened next, ending.

❖ Optional: an interesting or mysterious picture that represents the beginning of a story. There are commercially available pictures like this, or you could cut pictures out of the newspaper or magazines.

Aim	To generate ideas for sequential events in a story
Method	Tell the group that you are going to say the first line of a story and that everyone is going to help you to continue it. Say the first line, for example, 'One night I walked into a dark and scary house.' Use a story planner to prompt the next person in the group to think of the next part of the story. Continue around the group until you reach the end of the story. Encourage children to discuss if they think each idea makes sense and if they like their story.
Making it harder	Use a more complex structure for the story planner, for example: setting, event, problem, solution, ending. Do not use a picture card for the story, which will to encourage the children to use their imagination. Take away the story planner. .

Sequencing & Narrative in the Classroom

A child's school day presents them with many situations in which they need to be able to sequence and organise their thoughts. This allows lots of opportunities to develop sequencing skills. Stories and narratives are also encountered at least once a day at school. Here are some ways to make the most of these opportunities in order to support children to develop their sequencing and narrative skills.

1 Use a visual timetable in the classroom to show the sequence of events across the day. A visual timetable is only effective when adults and children actually engage with it. Show the symbol of the activity or lesson as it is about to start and when it ends. Get children to engage with the timetable by asking them to remove symbols when the activity has finished, so they can see what is coming next.

2 Use visuals such as photographs or symbols to represent the stages of a familiar routine, for example, getting ready for lunchtime. Mix up the pictures and ask the class to reorder them correctly. This technique will also be useful to help prepare children for unfamiliar events, for example, a school production, sports day or a school trip.

3 Write up bullet points or use pictures to represent each part of a lesson, for example: 'pens, paper, ruler, draw graph, write words underneath'. This acts as a visual schedule to help children to organise and sequence their actions, and will help them to work more independently.

4 When children need to explain or write up a report of something that has happened in the past, use photos or pictures to create a visual sequence. This will help children to remember the steps that were involved and will help their narratives to be much more meaningful and accurate.

5 Use concrete visual representations of time, such as sand timers, pictures of different clock times, or countdown timers on an interactive whiteboard. Link these to rewarding activities, for example, 'The clock says 10 more minutes of work and then it is break time.'

6 Ask children to retell stories that have been read to them. Use the pictures in books as a prompt. When they are talking, prompt them to use sequential language like 'then' and 'so', and 'finally'.

Phonological Awareness

Phonological awareness is the ability to process and manipulate the sounds of speech. It is a skill that helps with the development of literacy and speech production. Before children can read and write they need an awareness that sentences consist of words, and that words are made of syllables and sounds. Being able to break up words into sounds and recognise rhyme supports children to understand sound patterns in words. When working on phonological awareness in these activities, the focus is on the sounds in the words, rather than the letters used in written form. It is therefore important to use the letter sound rather than letter name. For example, the spoken word 'pie' starts with 'p' rather than 'pee'. Similarly 'egg' starts with a hard 'e' sound rather than 'ee'.

Indicators of Difficulty with Phonological Awareness

Children who have difficulties with phonological awareness may display these features:

❖ struggling with learning letter sounds;

❖ literacy skills that are slow to develop;

❖ difficulty with identifying words that rhyme or making up rhymes;

❖ counting the number of syllables in words is difficult;

❖ difficulty identifying the first sound in a word; and

❖ unclear speech because of speech sound delay.

Phonological Awareness Targets

1 To identify the number of syllables in a word

2 To say words that begin with a given sound

3 To identify words that rhyme

4 To add on words that rhyme

Clapping Names

Expected Time
Quick

Resources needed
None

Challenge level
Beginner

Aim	To identify the syllables in familiar words
Method	Start by modelling to the group how to clap the sounds in your own name. Say 'My name is', and then clap the number of syllables in your name. For example, 'My name is Sa-rah' (two claps). Continue around the group with each child having a turn to clap the syllables in their name, for example: Sa-man-tha (3 claps), and Paul (1 clap).
Helpful hint	One syllable words are harder for children to hear the beats in. Children whose name has one syllable may need some extra prompting. Model clapping it to them and get them to count the claps they hear.
Making it harder	Clap other children's names.

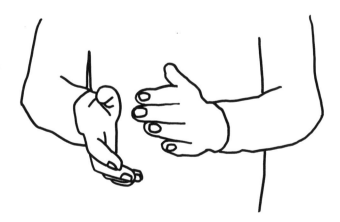

Clapping Animals

Expected Time
Quick

Resources needed
Pictures of familiar animals. Toys could also be used.

Challenge level
Beginner

Aim	To identify the number of syllables in a word
Method	Place the animal pictures in the middle of the group. Ask each child to name one of the pictures to check that the animals are familiar. Tell the group that you are going to clap the name of one of the animals in the pictures, and they have to guess which one it is. Clap the syllable beats of one of the animal names, without saying the name, for example 'elephant' would be three claps. The children have to put their hand up if they think they know which animal it was. Then it is the children's turn to clap the beats for the others in the group to guess. Continue around the group until everyone has had as turn at clapping.
Making it easier	Have only one animal picture for each different syllable length (e.g., a pig, a rabbit and a kangaroo), so the choices of animals are more obvious.
Making it harder	Increase the number of animal pictures on the table.

What I Had for Breakfast

Expected Time Quick	**Resources needed** None

Challenge level Intermediate

Aim	To identify the initial sound and the number of syllables in a word To think of a word when given clues about its initial sound and syllables
Method	Tell the group that you will give them a clue about what you had for breakfast. Say the first sound in the word and clap the number of syllables. For example, for Weetabix, say 'w' and clap three times. Ask the children to guess what it was. Go around the group with each child having a turn at giving clues about their breakfast. There is more than one possibility for each combination of sounds and syllables, so encourage the group to keep guessing if they do not get it right the first time; for example, 't' and one clap might be toast or tea.
Making it harder	Select a different category such as transport (e.g., 'How I got to school'), or fruits (e.g., 'My favourite fruit').

Beginning Sound

<table>
<tr><td>

Expected Time
Quick

Challenge level
Intermediate

</td><td>

Resources needed
Paper or whiteboard to write the sound on. A symbol that represents the chosen sound could also be used; for example, a snake for 's', and an ant for 'a'.

</td></tr>
</table>

Aim	To think of words that begin with a given sound
Method	Choose a sound to focus on in the session. If this is one of the sounds the children have been focusing on in the classroom this activity will be even more useful. Write the sound down to provide a visual cue and say the sound aloud. Go around the group and ask each child to say a word that begins with that sound. If children are struggling to think of their own word, offer them a choice of two words (e.g., 'Which one starts with "s", "see" or "tea"?').
Helpful hint	Remember that some words begin with the same letter, but take the sound of another sound. For example, cereal and ceiling both begin with 'c' but take the 's' sound, and cake and colour begin with 'c' but take the 'k' sound. Focus on the sound, not the letter in this activity.
Making it easier	Provide small picture cards showing words beginning with different sounds. The children can then choose a word that starts with the target sound rather than having to think of one for themselves.

I Went to Scotland

Expected Time
Quick

Challenge level
Intermediate

Resources needed
Paper or whiteboard to write the sound on. A symbol that represents the chosen sound could also be used; for example, a snake for 's', and an ant for 'a'.

Aim	To think of words within a category that start with a given letter
Method	Start the game by choosing a target sound and a place that starts with that sound, for example, 'Scotland' and 's'. Explain that you are going to talk about all the things that you bought when you went on a holiday to Scotland. The words all need to start with the same sound as the place, for example, 'I went to Scotland and I bought a sock.' Go around the group and ask the children to add items that also start with that sound, for example, 'I went to Scotland and I bought some skis.' Continue adding words until everyone has had at least one turn. Change the place that was visited to somewhere beginning with a different sound, for example, 'I went to Turkey and I bought a table.'

Phonological Awareness

My Big Brain

Expected Time
Quick

Resources needed
None

Challenge level
Intermediate

Aim To generate words in a given category that start with a particular sound

Method This game is like 'I Spy', but instead of talking about things that can be seen, the words must belong to a category. Choose a letter sound and a category of words, for example, food, drinks, sports, countries. Think of a word but do not tell the group what it is. Start off the game by saying, 'I think with my big brain ...' For example, 'I think with my big brain, of a drink beginning with "s"'. Go around the group and ask the children to take turns at guessing what it is. Once it has been guessed, it is the first child's turn to think of a new word. Keep the same category for the whole activity.

Willaby Wallaby

Aim   To identify words that rhyme with a child's own name

Method   Tell the group that you will say a verse (below), which has a word that rhymes with someone in the group's name. For example: 'Willaby Wallaby Woyce, a wallaby sat on …'. Pause and wait for the child whose name rhymes with 'Woyce' to recognise this, e.g. 'Joyce'. Nonsense rhyming words are acceptable. If the child recognises that their name rhymes with that word, they can finish the rhyme by saying their name. Then take the wallaby toy and pretend to sit it on that child. Continue saying the rhyme and until there has been one for everyone's name. Another example is: 'Willaby Wallaby Wate, a wallaby sat on [Kate].'

Phonological Awareness

Find the Rhyme

Expected Time Quick	**Resources needed**
Challenge level Beginner	❖ A set of picture cards with pairs of words that rhyme. There are commercially available sets of these picture cards, or they can easily be made. ❖ An opaque bag

Aim	To match words that rhyme
Method	Place half of the cards in an opaque bag and spread the other half out on the table. Show the children what they have to do by taking one picture from the bag, naming it aloud and then finding a rhyming picture from the ones on the table. The children have to take turns at doing the same. Continue around the group until all of the pictures have been used.
Making it harder	Once the child has matched the rhyming pair, encourage them to add two more rhyming words, for example, man, van, can and pan.

Listen for the Rhyme

Expected Time Quick	**Resources needed** Prepare a list of rhyming words and non-rhyming words to be read out aloud.
Challenge level Beginner	

Aim	To listen and judge if two words rhyme
Method	Explain to the group that they are going to hear two words. If the words rhyme, the children must stand up. If the words do not rhyme, they should stay sitting down. Call out pairs of words (e.g., pat and mat), but also include some pairs that do not rhyme (e.g., log and peg).
Making it harder	To encourage the children to listen carefully for rhyming words, include some words in the non-rhyming pairs that have the same initial sound (e.g., bee and bear). Also include longer words, for example, basement and casement.

Rhyming Names

Expected Time Quick	**Resources needed** None
Challenge level Intermediate	

Aim

To be able to identify and generate words that rhyme with familiar names

Method

Explain to the group that everyone is going to choose someone else's name to say, but with a rhyme. Model the first example to the group. Choose a child's name (e.g., Sally), but instead say a name that rhymes with it (e.g., 'I choose Dally'). Nonsense words are acceptable. If that child recognises that the word rhymes with their name, then it is their turn. They need to choose someone else and make a rhyme for that person's name. Continue around the group a few times so that children hear different words that their names rhyme with.

Guess the Rhyming Word

Expected Time
Quick

Resources needed
A selection of familiar objects or picture cards

Challenge level
Intermediate

Aim	To identify and generate words that rhyme with a picture or object
Method	Lay the objects out in the middle of the group. Tell everyone to choose an item and keep it in their head. They are not allowed to point to it or pick it up yet. Everyone will say the object they have chosen by saying a word that rhymes with it. Give the children an example: for a sock say, 'Dock.' The children then guess which object it is. Ask the first child to do the same, making up their own rhyming word for their chosen object. Nonsense words are acceptable. Continue going around the group so that everyone has a turn.

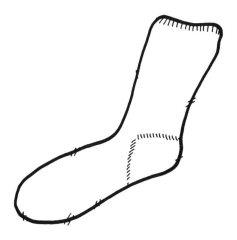

Pass the Rhyme

Expected Time
Quick

Challenge level
Intermediate

Resources needed
❖ Opaque bag
❖ A selection of familiar and interesting objects

Aim	To generate words that rhyme with a given object
Method	Choose a child to start the game, and ask them to take an object out of the bag. They have to say what it is, and give a word that rhymes with it. Nonsense words are acceptable, for example, 'It's a pen, and a rhyming word is "len"'. The object is then passed around the group and each person has to think of a different rhyming word (e.g., men, ten, ken). Once everyone has thought of a rhyming word, it is the next child's turn to take out a new object.

Finish the Rhyme

Expected Time
Quick

Resources needed
None

Challenge level
Intermediate

Aim	To identify a word that rhymes with the last word in a sentence
Method	Give the group a starter sentence, leaving off the final word. Explain to the group that they need to finish the sentence with a rhyming word to make it sound like a poem; for example, 'One day I walked along the *road*, and I saw a great big ....' Pause. Each child takes a turn to suggest a rhyming word to finish the sentence (toad, load or code). Continue around the group, and once everyone has suggested an appropriate rhyming word give a new starter sentence.

Phonological Awareness in the Classroom

The classroom is the ideal environment to focus on developing pre-literacy skills. Children with speech production difficulties and delayed communication skills will need more opportunities to build their sound knowledge, as they are at risk of having difficulties with reading and writing. Here are some ways to support those children to develop phonological awareness in the classroom.

1 Highlight children's need to listen to sounds in general. These do not just have to be speech sounds. Encourage the class to listen carefully and respond to music, sounds in the environment, or recordings of sounds.

2 Ensure that children can see your face when you are teaching sounds in words. Encourage them to look at your mouth shape as it gives useful clues about the sound you are making. Explain what to do with your mouth to make a sound. For example, if teaching the sound 'f', explain that you need to put your top teeth on your bottom lip and push the air out.

3 Use a multisensory approach when introducing sounds in words. Say the sound, use a gesture, and listen to someone else say the sound. Encourage children to touch their throat to feel their voice when making quiet (e.g., 't') or loud sounds (e.g., 'd'), and clap out the beats in longer words.

4 Some children may not be able to produce a sound but can hear and recognise it. For children who have speech difficulties, allow them to show their knowledge of sounds by providing letters or pictures for them to point to.

Social Communication

Social communication is a key part of a child's language development. Social language skills are needed to understand social situations and to communicate with others in order to make friends. Social communication also incorporates pragmatics, which is the way language is used to interact with others. Some children do not develop these skills naturally, and need to learn and practise them in a specific way. These activities give an opportunity to practise social communication in a safe group environment, so that they can then go on to use these skills in more natural environments like the playground or classroom. It is very important to consider ways to support the children to transfer these skills from the group to other settings.

Indicators of Difficulty with Social Communication

Children who have difficulties with social communication may present with these features:

❖ difficulty understanding other people's feelings;

❖ giving too much or too little information in conversations;

❖ problems initiating or continuing conversations;

❖ difficulties making appropriate eye contact;

❖ finding taking turns and sharing equipment difficult;

❖ interrupting during conversation;

❖ difficulties making and maintaining friendships; and

❖ difficulty with managing a communication breakdown.

Social Communication Targets

1 To make and maintain eye contact appropriately with others

2 To respond to and use social greetings

3 To participate in group activities non-verbally

4 To wait and take turns

5 To answer questions about yourself

6 To recognise and use facial expressions linked to emotions

7 To understand positive differences between people, such as their peers' interests or strengths

8 To identify situations that are linked to different emotions

9 To role play familiar social situations

10 To recognise when they have not understood an instruction and request a clarification

11 To ask and answer specific questions in a group situation

12 To explain solutions to familiar social problems

13 To recognise appropriate and inappropriate social communication in others

14 To role play using appropriate social communication

Social Communication

Where Are You?

Expected Time
Quick

Resources needed
Scarf, a piece of netting, or other light fabric

Challenge level
Beginner

Aim	To make eye contact with peers in a group
Method	Choose a child to start and lightly place the scarf over their head. Sing a tune with the child's name, for example, 'Lucas, Lucas, where are you?' Wait for child to pull off scarf or help them to do this. Establish eye contact and then sing, 'There you are, there you are, how do you do?

It's Me!

Expected Time	**Resources needed**
Quick	None

Challenge level
Beginner

Aim	To make eye contact and interact verbally with peers
Method	Tell the group that you are going to close your eyes and then look at someone. The children will need to be looking to see if it is them. Close your eyes and count out loud to three. Open your eyes and look directly at one child. Keep eye contact and say, 'Who am I looking at?' When the child notices the adult looking at them, they have to say 'It's me!' Keep repeating this sequence until all the children have been looked at.
Making it easier	For children who are not yet using spoken language, accept a gesture such as pointing at themselves rather saying the phrase.
Making it harder	The children take turns at being the person who looks.

Shake My Hand

Expected Time Quick	**Resources needed** None

Challenge level
 Beginner

Aim	To respond to and initiate a social greeting with peers
Method	This game should be played at the start of the group session. Start by taking the hand of the first child and shaking it. Make eye contact and say 'hello'. That child then has to shake the hand of person to their left, and says 'hello'. Once everyone has had a turn, ask the children to all hold hands. Count to three and say 'hello everyone!'
Making it easier	Sing a song to match this game, such as 'Shake my hand, shake my hand, shake my hand and say hello!'

Everybody Do This

Expected Time
Quick

Challenge level
Beginner

Resources needed
Cards with pictures of people doing different actions (optional)

Aim	To join in and copy actions
Method	Choose a card from a pile of action pictures or think of an action; for example, clapping, brushing teeth, tapping knees. Mime doing the action repeatedly, and sing 'Everybody do this, do this, do this. Everybody do this, just like me.' Encourage the children to look and copy the actions.
Making it harder	Ask the children to name the action. When they are familiar with the game, the children can take turns to lead.

Pass the Look

Expected Time
Quick

Resources needed
None

Challenge level
Beginner

Aim	To use eye contact and take turns
Method	Choose a child to go first and look directly at them. Explain to the group that you are looking at someone, and now the 'look' has to be passed around the group. The child must then pass the look by looking into the eyes of the person beside them. Encourage the group to keep looking so they are ready when the look is passed to them. Continue around the group a few times.
Making it harder	When the pupils are familiar with good eye contact, try passing the look across the group.

What Do You Like?

Expected Time
Quick

Resources needed
None

Challenge level
Beginner

Aim	To ask and answer questions about own interests
Method	Choose a topic and tell the group what it is, for example, food. Start by saying something you like from that topic, for example, 'I like chips.' Turn to a child and ask them, 'What do you like?' They have to answer with something they like from that topic. This is continued around the group, with each person answering then asking the question. Other topics could include TV shows, games, sports, colours, or football teams.
Making it harder	Ask the children to explain why they like that thing, for example, 'I like Ben 10 because Ben does lots of tricks.'

Social Communication

Pass the Emotion

Expected Time
Quick

Challenge level
Intermediate

Resources needed
Emotion picture cards: photos or pictures of people showing a range of facial expressions or body language that clearly demonstrates their emotions. These are commercially available or they can easily be drawn or made.

Aim	To make facial expressions to convey a range of emotions
Method	Take one emotion picture card at a time and ask the group to say how the person in the picture feels. Go through all the cards to establish if the children can recognise the facial expressions. Ask the first child to choose a card and copy the facial expression on it. They show this facial expression to the child next to them and that child then has to copy the face. This continues around the group so the emotion is 'passed' on to each person. Once the emotion has been passed around once, then the next child can choose a new emotion card.
Making it harder	Ask the group to think of their own emotion words and make the facial expressions without using picture prompts.

Pass the Compliment

Expected Time
Quick

Resources needed
None

Challenge level
Intermediate

Aim	To give compliments to each other
Method	Explain to the group that a compliment is when you tell a person something that is good about them. Model giving the first child a compliment, for example, 'You are great at drawing.' That child then has to turn to the person next to them and give them a compliment. Continue around the group so that everyone has given and received a compliment.
Helpful hint	This game works best once the group has been running for a few sessions when the children know each other better.

Match Our Interests

Expected Time Mid-length	**Resources needed** ❖ Pencils for each child ❖ Small pieces of paper ❖ A box
Challenge level Intermediate	

Aim	To show an awareness of other children's interests
Method	Give each child a piece of paper. They have to write down three things that they like doing or talking about. These are all then placed in the box and mixed around. Choose a child to select the first piece of paper. They have to read out the topics that are written and then try to guess who wrote it. Encourage the group to think of what they know about each other. If their first guess is wrong, they have to put the paper back in the box and it is passed on to the next person.
Helpful hint	This game works best once the group has been running for a few sessions when the children know each other better.
Making it easier	Help children who have difficulties with writing by scribing their interest for them.

The Present Game

Expected Time
Mid-length

Challenge level
Intermediate

Resources needed
A mixture of pictures of items that would be given as a birthday present. Toy catalogues are a good place to look for these pictures. Make them into small cards.

Aim	To understand peers' interests and preferences
Method	Spread the pictures out on the table so that everyone can see them. Explain that these are presents for everyone in the group, and that they have to choose which present they think the person next to them would like. Ask each child in turn to pick up a picture and give it to the person on their left. They must also say why it would be a good present for that person, for example, 'I'm giving you a pair of trainers because you're a good footballer.' If the group do not know each other very well, start off the session with everyone saying something about their interests and favourite things. This will help the children to choose an appropriate present.

Emotions Dice

<table>
<tr><td>

Expected Time
Mid-length

Challenge level
Intermediate

</td><td>

Resources needed
A dice with six faces showing different emotions. There is a template for Emotions Dice in the Resources section, p. 218. Alternatively take a large dice and stick pictures of different facial expressions on it.

</td></tr>
</table>

Aim	To identify emotions from line drawings, and to think of situations linked to these emotions
Method	The children take turns at rolling the dice. The child whose turn it is has to name the emotion that matches the facial expression on the dice. Ask the child to copy the facial expression and think of a situation that might make someone feel that way. For example, if they roll 'angry' they could say, 'When my brother steals my Playstation games.' Continue around the group so that everyone has had a chance to roll the dice.

Winking Witch

Expected Time
Mid-length

Challenge level
Intermediate

Resources needed
❖ Folded pieces of blank paper (one for each player). One piece of paper must have a picture of witch on it (this can be drawn).
❖ Box to keep the papers in

Aim
To maintain eye contact
To participate in a role play
To make deductions based on observation

Method
Choose one child in the group to be the 'detective', who has to stand up. Pass around the box with the papers in it. Every child except the detective takes a piece of folded paper and looks at it. Explain that if they have a blank piece of paper they are potential victims of the 'winking witch'. If their paper has the picture of the witch, then they *are* the winking witch and they must keep this a secret. Explain that the winking witch has a special power of making people fall into a deep sleep when she winks at them. Tell the group that the game has now started and the detective is going to try to find the winking witch. The witch starts to wink at people and they must then pretend to fall into a deep sleep . The witch must try to not get caught by the detective. The detective must use good eye contact and look carefully at each person to try to identify who the witch is. The group members and the witch must keep good eye contact with each other and try not to make it obvious as to who the witch is. Repeat with a different detective each time.

Fix Up the Instructions

Expected Time
Lengthy

Resources needed
A selection of familiar small objects

Challenge level
Intermediate

Aim	For children to recognise what was wrong with an instruction and request a clarification
Method	Place some of the objects in the middle of the group. Start by giving each child a simple instruction to follow, for example, 'Jodie, give the ball to Mia.' Continue with some more 'good' instructions then, after a few have been given, deliberately make the instructions difficult to follow. Ways to do this could include talking too quietly, too fast, in a mumbled way, or with too many complicated words. Ask the children what was wrong with the instruction. The children then need to say what they would like you to to do in order for them to understand. For example, 'Could you say that again a bit slower?', 'I don't know what those words mean', or 'I couldn't hear you, can you say it again a bit louder?'
Making it easier	Before giving the instructions, write down the different ways that they might be hard to understand. The children can use these as visual prompts for what they need to say when they have not understood.

Thirty-Second Talk

Expected Time
Lengthy

Challenge level
Advanced

Resources needed
❖ Pieces of paper with topics of interest written on them. Topics could include favourite TV shows, Playstation games, sports, a holiday.
❖ A box
❖ A watch or clock with a second hand

Aim	To talk about a given topic for an extended length of time. To ask and answer questions about the information shared
Method	Put the pieces of paper with the topics into a box. Choose a child to go first. They select a topic and then have to talk about it for thirty seconds. Tell them to start talking, but remind them to stay on the topic. If they are struggling to think of what to say, ask open prompt questions, such as, 'Why do you like it'?, and 'Tell us everything you know about it.' Once they have finished talking, the other children have to ask one question each to find out some more information, for example, 'When did you do that?' After the questions it is another child's turn to choose a new topic and talk. Continue around the group so that everyone has a turn to talk.
Making it easier	Reduce the time that the children have to talk, starting at around ten seconds. Or allow children to choose their own topic of interest.
Making it harder	Extend the time that children talk about a topic.

Real-Life Role Play

Expected Time Lengthy	**Resources needed** None

Challenge level Advanced

Aim To act out familiar social situations. To discuss emotions and potential solutions.

Method Ask the group to think of experiences at school that have made them excited, upset, angry, happy, or confused. Prompt them to think about things that have happened in the playground. If the group has difficulty thinking of their own ideas, use some fictional examples. There are some examples of social problems on the Simple Solutions Cards in the Resources section, p. 213.

Choose a positive event to role play first (e.g., 'I found out that I had been chosen to represent the school in a chess tournament'), before moving on to difficult social situations (e.g., 'The girls I usually play with wouldn't let me join in skipping'). Ask one child to describe what happened in detail, so that everyone is familiar with the situation. Ask the group to think about who was involved and allocate children to play different roles. Start acting out the event. Tell the group to freeze and stop the acting at different points. Discuss how each person would be feeling at that point. Ask the children to think what should happen next.

Helpful hint Gain permission to video the role play and watch it back as a group. Stop the play at particular points and discuss what should happen next.

Fix Up the Role Play

Expected Time	Resources needed
Lengthy	None

Challenge level
Advanced

Aim	For children to identify inappropriate social skills and act out the appropriate alternative
Method	Ask one child to join you in a role play to the rest of the group. Warn the child doing the role play that you are going to act very strangely in order to demonstrate examples of inappropriate social interactions. These could include:

❖ inappropriate physical interaction (e.g., poor eye contact, lots of fidgeting, standing too close);

❖ not taking turns in conversation, interrupting and talking over the other person;

❖ speaking at the inappropriate volume for the context (i.e. too quiet or too loud);

❖ waiting a long time to start a conversation, or ending one abruptly; and

❖ going off the topic in conversation, or not taking into account what the other person wants to talk about.

When each role play is finished, ask the group what was wrong with the interaction. What could be done differently? The children then have a turn at practising the right and the wrong way to use a particular social skill. Choose another child to be involved in the role play with you and repeat.

Helpful hint	Choose examples of social skills that are particularly relevant for the needs of the children in the group.

Social Communication in the Classroom

The classroom provides an opportunity to model and encourage good social communication for those children who have difficulties. Use real experiences in the social environment of a large group of children to reinforce appropriate social skills. Here are some specific ways to support good social communication in the classroom.

1 Make specific rules for good communication during classroom discussions, such as 'no interrupting', 'hands up if you have a question' and 'look at the person talking'. Use symbols or pictures to display the rules and regularly reinforce them with the whole class. The group rules referred to in this book are appropriate to use in the classroom as class rules, especially for younger classes (see Resources, Group Rules Card, p. 198).

2 Create opportunities for children to have focused conversations in groups or pairs. Encourage discussion through the use of talk partners and allow time for the children to report back on what was said to the wider group. It is important that children feel confident with talking quietly to a peer, but also to the larger group. Pair up children with social communication difficulties with children whose skills are more developed.

3 During group work nominate a child to be the social communication monitor. This child walks around and observes and rates if the class is following the rules of good communication. Provide them with a monitoring sheet with a list of the class communication rules. They can report back to the group and remind people about which rules they need to use. Getting this feedback from a peer can be more powerful than hearing it from an adult.

4 Get children to support less confident peers in the playground by setting up a rotating buddy system. The buddy can look out for a particular child and ensure they are included in playground games.

5 During circle time or class discussion talk about social situations or problems that are familiar to the children (there are some examples of these in Simple Solutions Cards in the Resources section, p. 213). Ask children about how the people would feel and ask for possible solutions. Discuss the pros and cons of each solution, emphasising that there are often several options.

Social Communication in the Classroom

6 Use role play where possible, so that the children can gain a greater insight into other people's perspectives.

7 Use social situations from books or films that the class have been looking at. Discuss the feelings and problems for the characters involved. Choose a child to be in the 'hot seat', in which one child takes on the view of a character and is quizzed by others.

Part Two
Resources

Group Rules Cards

good listening

wait for your turn

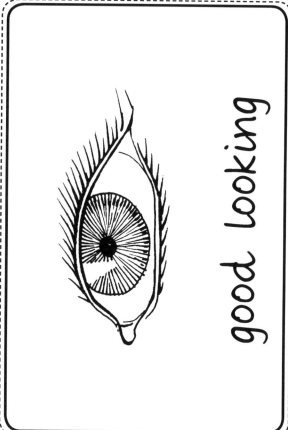

good looking

good sitting

Children in group: _____

TARGETS	Dates							
❖								
❖								
❖								
❖								
❖								

E = exceeded; F = fully met; P = partially met; N = not met

Sample Communication Group Record Sheet

Children in group: James, Tolu, Rory

TARGETS	Dates	20.09.10	23.09.10					
❖ All children will be able to show 'good sitting' and 'good looking' during the group, with verbal and visual prompts (e.g., rules card/gesture)		James: P Tolu: P Rory: N	James: M Tolu: P Rory: N					
❖ All children will be able to name 3 items from the category 'plants'.		James: M Tolu: M Rory: P	James: E Tolu: M Rory: P					
❖ Rory will follow instructions with 3 key words including 'in'/'on'/'under' e.g., 'put the <u>star</u> <u>in</u> the <u>bag</u>' (with a choice of items for the underlined words)		Rory: N	Rory: P					
❖ James and Tolu will follow instructions with 4 key words, including 'big'/'little' and 'in'/'on'/'under' e.g., 'put the <u>big</u> <u>star</u> <u>under</u> the <u>hat</u>' (with a choice of items for the underlined words)		James: M Tolu: N	James: M Tolu: N					
❖ All children will name one activity that they have remembered from the group session		James: M Tolu: M Rory: P	James: M Tolu: P Rory: P					

E = exceeded; F = fully met; P = partially met; N = not met

Your Child is in a Communication Group – What is it?

A language group is a regular, safe, friendly and fun environment where children can learn and explore language and build their confidence in communicating.

It also provides a way that they can develop and practise important foundation skills for language and learning, such as listening and turn taking.

Communication skills that can be developed in these groups include:

❖ Listening skills

❖ Understanding and following instructions

❖ Telling stories

❖ Using the right words (vocabulary)

❖ Holding information in memory

❖ Explaining how to solve problems

❖ Interaction and social skills

A communication group is often planned with a speech and language therapist (SLT), according to the strengths and needs of the children in the group. The group may be run by a member of school staff, such as a teaching assistant, and usually takes place once or twice per week.

Page 1 of 2

Parent Handout

Your Child is in a Communication Group – What is it?

Your child will be set specific targets during the group. This helps staff to monitor their progress and to make sure that the group is as effective as possible for working on their language and communication needs.

Communication group activities may include the following:

❖ Following instructions to draw a detailed picture

❖ Memory games

❖ Answering questions about what is happening in a picture

❖ Describing pictures in a sequence to make a story

❖ 'Guess the word' games

Your child is in a group which is led by _____

It is run at these times:

_____

_____

Your child is working towards these targets:

_____

_____

_____

If you have any questions about this communication group you can contact us on:

_____

Page 2 of 2

Template for Visual Timetable

Instructions

❖ Draw or insert your own symbols in the boxes below.

❖ Cut the boxes up and attach them to card or laminate the paper.

❖ Use Blu-tack® or Velcro® to stick the symbols to a larger piece of card.

❖ When an activity is completed the children can pull off the symbol and stick them on the back to indicate that it has finished.

❖ Alternatively, you could make a little box or bag and call it the 'finished bag', and when an activity is finished the symbols are placed in the bag.

Warm-Up Game	
Target Activity 1	
Target Activity 2	
Target Activity 3	
Finishing Activity	
Goodbye	

Self-Rating Chart for Group Targets

Name: _____

My Rating	Date:	Date:	Date:	Date:	Date:	Date:
↑ 1 2 3						
Target 1						
Target 2						
Target 3						
Target 4						

'I am Working For ...' Chart

Instructions

❖ Copy this template onto card or laminate.

❖ Put Velcro® on the back of the darker circles and on the white circles on the card so that they can be stuck together.

❖ Draw or attach a symbol to the large box to indicate what the reward will be.

❖ When a child has shown positive behaviour, stick one of the dark circles onto the white circles on their chart. This indicates that a reward has been given. Tell the child they are getting a token and show them what you are doing.

❖ It can be useful to show the child how many more circles they need to get in order to earn the reward.

❖ When all five circles have been filled, give the reward.

❖ Each child in the group could have one of these, or just the child who is having particular difficulties

| Name: |
| I am working for: |

Lotto Boards Template

Fill these boards with pictures of the words that you are working on in your group activity. They could be drawn, or use symbols or images from a computer programme. Use different combinations of the pictures for each person's lotto board so that each board is different. Then create lotto cards using copies of the same pictures, but cut up them up into single cards, ensuring enough for each player.

Fishing Game Template

Photocopy and cut up these fish, and use them for a fishing game. Attach small pictures to the fish with paper clips. To make a fishing rod, use a piece of dowel or a stick with string attached, and a magnet at the end of the string. The magnet will pick up the paper clip to 'catch' a fish.

Worksheet for Colouring Game

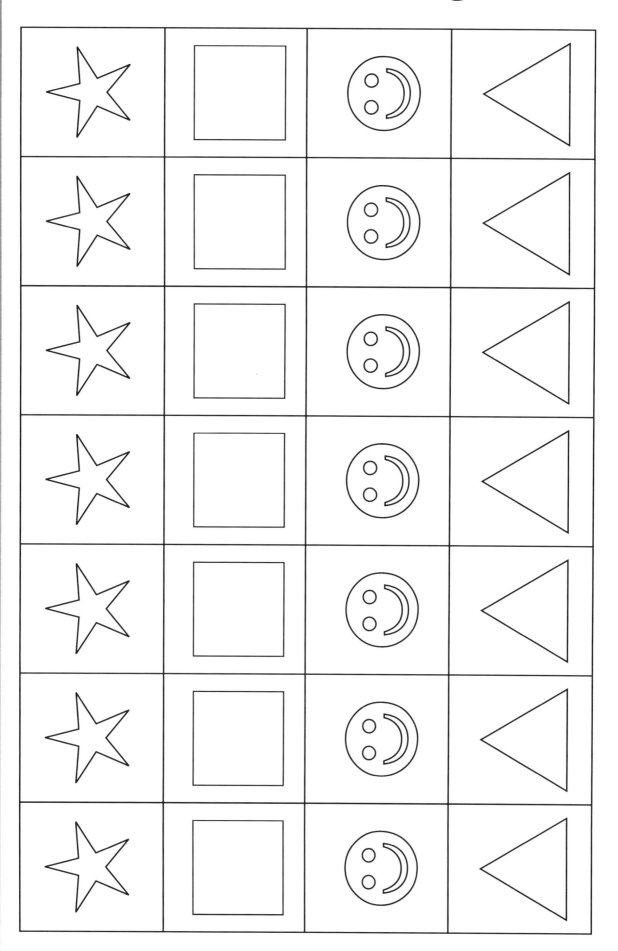

Plurals Lotto Board (i)

Use these boards to play 'Plurals Lotto' (see page 93 for full instructions). Make copies of the boards for each player, and then make extra copies of the boards which can be cut up into individual picture cards.

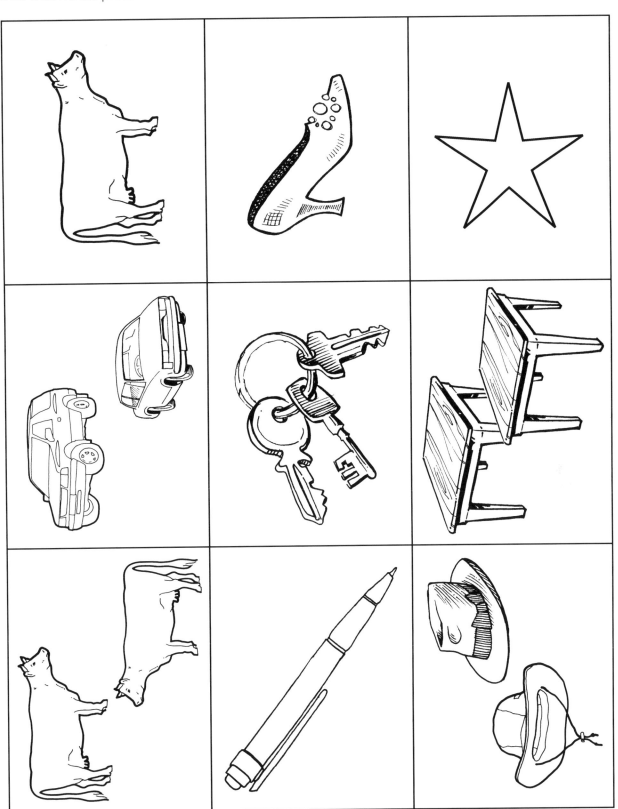

Plurals Lotto Board (ii)

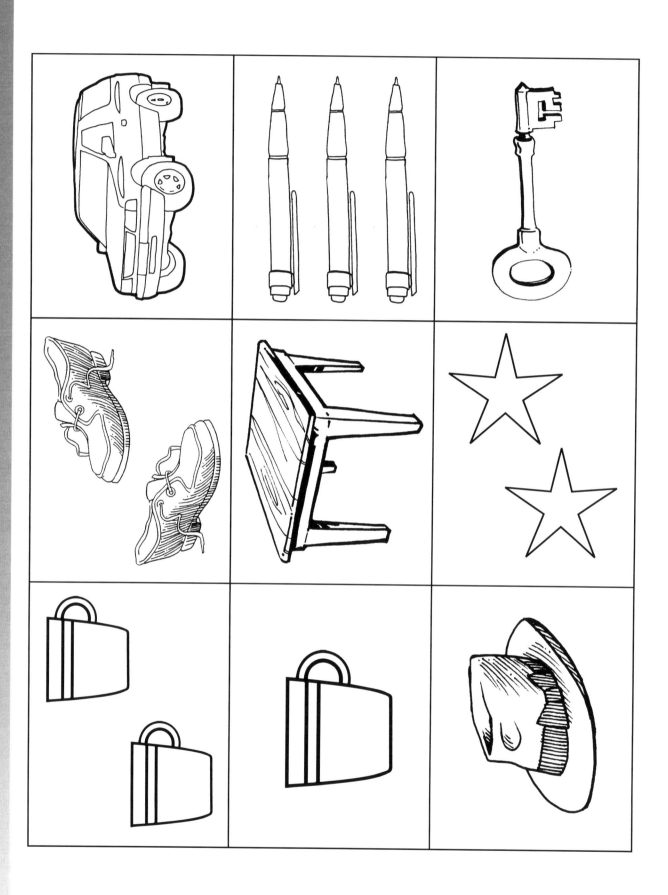

Instructions for Listen and Draw

1 Write your **age** at the **top** of the page, in the **middle**.

2 Write your **name** in the **bottom**, **left hand corner** of the page.

3 **Fold** your page in **half**, from **top** to **bottom**.

4 **Unfold** your page and draw a **line across the middle of the page**.

5 In the **top half** of your page, draw a **large circle** (it will be a face).

6 **Inside** your face, draw **two sandwiches** for **eyes**.

7 **Inside** your face, draw an **apple** for a **nose**.

8 **Inside** your face, draw a **banana**, **on its side** for a **smiling mouth**.

9 In the **bottom half** of your page, draw a **large rectangle**.

10 **Inside** your rectangle, write the **name** of your **pet**. If you **do not** have a **pet**, write your **favourite animal**.

11 On **top** of your **rectangle**, draw a **diamond** shape.

12 On the **bottom** of your **rectangle**, draw an **oval** shape.

Do your pictures look the same?

Why/Because Cards

Why should you say 'thank you' when someone hands you a pencil?	Why are children happy on Saturday mornings?	Why does every school have a head teacher?
Why do you get to sleep in longer on the weekends?	Why is it better to play outside than inside?	Why should dogs be kept on leads?
Why should you eat breakfast every morning?	Why do people have pets?	Why do you have to learn maths at school?
Why do we have to line up at the end of lunchtime?	Why do teachers check the register in the morning?	Why do we have to stay inside when it rains at playtime?
Why are we not allowed to play football in the hallway at school?	Why is bullying wrong?	Why is it nice to go to a birthday party?
Why do we have school holidays?	Why do some schools wear a school uniform?	Why do we have to do tests at school?

Simple Solutions Cards

What would you do if you arrived at school and no one else was there?	What would you do if you left your homework at home?	What would you do if you forgot your packed lunch?
What would you do if no one came to collect you after school?	What would you do if your best friend was in hospital?	What would you do if you saw your little brother playing with your favourite toy?
What would you do if you borrowed a game from your friend and you lost it?	What would you do if your mum gave you £10, but when you looked in your bag it was missing?	What would you do if you found £20 outside the school gate?
What would you do if your pen stopped working in the middle of a spelling test?	What would you do if you fell off your bike on the way to school and then you were late for class?	What would you do if it was the day of your friend's birthday party and you felt ill?
What would you do if you were playing football and you accidently hurt your friend's leg?	What would you do if you went on a school trip and you missed the bus back?	What would you do if someone pushed you over when lining up to go back to class?

Question Prompts

Who?

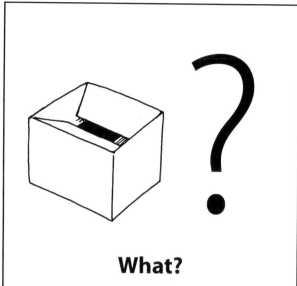

What?

When?

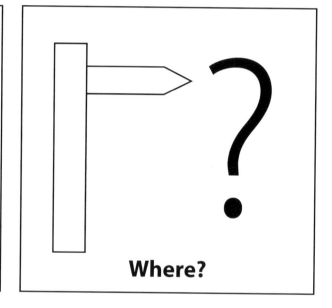

Where?

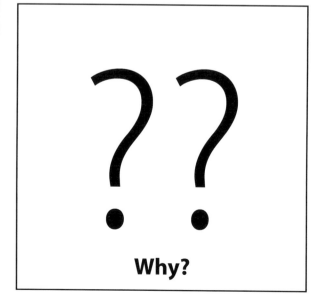

Why?

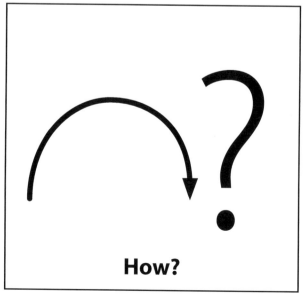

How?

Memory Strategy

1. Listen to the words

2. Take a photo in my brain

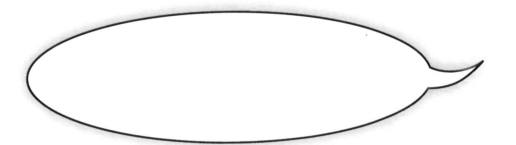

3. Say the words again to myself

4. Do it!

Describing Prompt Sheet

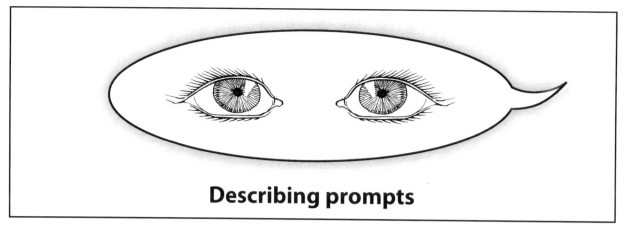

Describing prompts

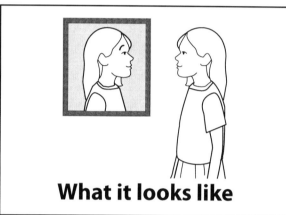

What it looks like

Where it goes

Group it belongs in

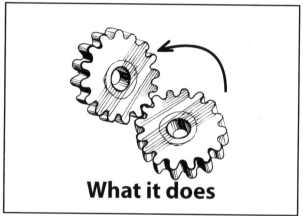

What it does

Sound it starts with

Something interesting

Sequential Language Prompts

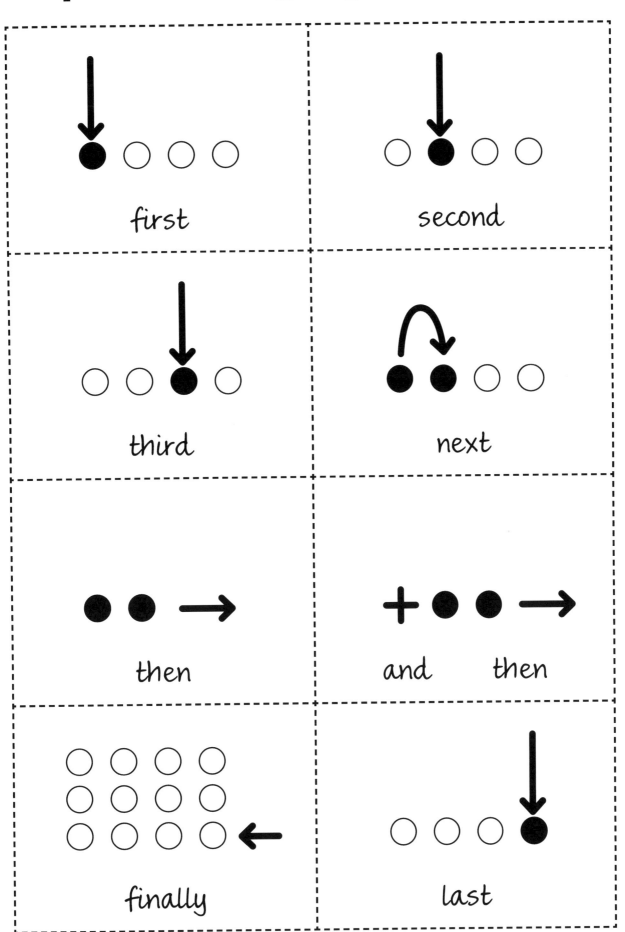

first

second

third

next

then

and   then

finally

last

Template for Emotions Dice

Cut out this template so you are left with a 't' shape. Laminate or stick it on to card, then tape the edges together to make a cube which can then be used as a die.

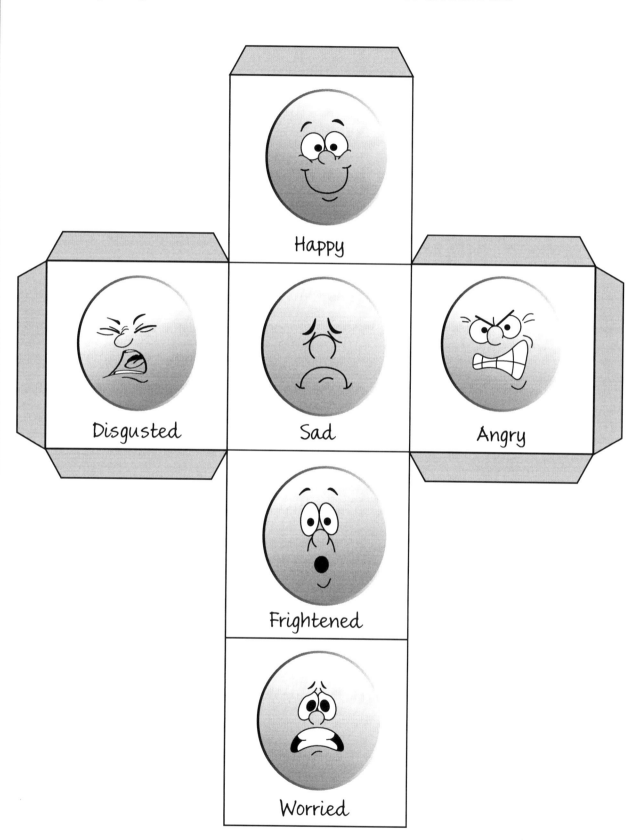

Super Talker

Awarded to

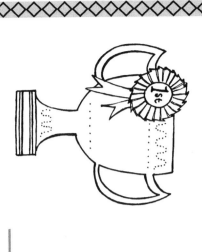

for attending the Communication Group this term.

You have made great progress with your skills. Well done!

Signed: _____

Name: _____

Group Leader

Signed: _____

Name: _____

Teacher

Date: _____

Index of Activities

The 50 Best Games series …

- ☼ These handy pocket books will ensure you are never again stuck for activity ideas that will help make both teaching and learning fun!

- ☼ Carefully selected, each collection of the 50 Best Games is themed and addresses a specific area of development. All the games are easy to implement with the minimum of preparation and can be adapted to the needs of your particular group.

- ☼ Use them as warm-ups, ice breakers, time fillers or to address a specific need. Suitable for groups of all sizes and can be used with all ages from young children to adolescents.

The 50 Best Games for Building Self-Esteem
Rosemarie Portmann
ISBN 978-0-906531-18-8

The 50 Best Games for Sensory Perception
ISBN 978-0-906531-11-9

The 50 Best Games for Brain Exercise
Rosemarie Portmann
ISBN 978-0-906531-14-0

The 50 Best Games for Relaxation & Concentration
Rosemarie Portmann
ISBN 978-0-906531-17-1

The 50 Best Games for Speech & Language Development
Maria Monschein
ISBN 978-0-906531-13-3

The 50 Best Games for Children's Groups
Birgit Fuchs
ISBN 978-0-906531-12-6

The 50 Best Games for Groups
Josef Griesbeck
ISBN 978-0-906531-16-4

The 50 Best Indoor Games for Groups
Josef Griesbeck
ISBN 978-0-906531-15-7

www.hintonpublishers.com

Index